SALE NUMBER 4390

IMPORTANT SILVER

Property from the Estates of Mabel Brady Garvan, New York
Donald S. Morrison, New Jersey
Property of Pearl D. Morrison, New Jersey

Including

Elizabeth I Beaker, London, 1599
James I Beaker, London, 1609
Pair of Queen Anne silver-gilt Covered Bowls, Pierre Platel, London, circa 1710
Two Matching George II Salvers engraved with the Exchequer Seal of George II and
the Seal of The Prince of Wales, subsequently George II, London, 1728 and 1735
Silver by Paul de Lamerie, including a rectangular Tray, 1741
Group of Early Eighteenth Century Tapersticks
Irish Silver including a George II quatrefoil Salver, John Hamilton, Dublin, 1737
George III Miniature Tea Set, London, 1818

Dutch Beaker, Nijmegen, 1615
Dutch Beaker, Workum, circa 1650

EXHIBITION

Saturday, May 31, 1980 from 10 a.m. to 5 p.m.
Monday, June 2, from 10 a.m. to 4 p.m.
Tuesday and Wednesday, June 3 and 4 from 10 a.m. to 5 p.m.
Thursday, June 5, from 10 a.m. to 3 p.m.

PUBLIC AUCTION

Friday, June 6, 1980 at 2 p.m.

SOTHEBY PARKE BERNET INC.

980 Madison Avenue (76th–77th Streets)
New York 10021 (212) 472-3400
Cable: Parkgal, New York
Telex: New York 232643 (SOL UR)

Recorded Announcement of Current Sales and Exhibitions, 24 hours a day: 212-472-3555

Cover Illustration: Lot 24, detail

Sotheby Parke Bernet Inc · New York

ADMINISTRATION

Chairman & President
John L. Marion, 472-3426
Chief Operating Officer
Frederick H. Scholtz, 472-4862
Finance & Administration
Arnold M. Kagan, 472-3434
Special Sales & Real Estate
Edward Lee Cave, 472-3431

Appraisals & Estates
C. Hugh Hildesley, 472-3454
Director of Sales, Fine Arts
David J. Nash, 472-3590
Communications & Promotion
Thomas E. Norton, 472-3424
Director of Sales, Decorative Arts
Robert C. Woolley, 472-3503

Paintings Department Director
Mary-Anne Martin, 472-4766
Treasurer
Alan M. Forster, 472-3443
Controller
Howard Weiss, 472-3441
Regional Auction Centers, Director
John D. Block, 472-3568

Assistant to the President
Nancy A. Forster, 472-3426
General Counsel & Secretary
Mitchell Zuckerman, Esq.
472-3476
Museum Services
Susan L. Brody, 472-3478

EXPERT DEPARTMENTS

American Decorative Arts & Furniture
William W. Stahl, 472-3511
American Folk Art
Nancy Druckman, 472-3512
American Indian Art
Ellen Napiura, 472-3522
American Paintings
Peter B. Rathbone
Grete Meilman, 472-3551
Antiquities, African & Oceanic Art
Richard M. Keresey, 472-3521
Books & Manuscripts
Stuart Bennett, 472-3593
Thomas P. Clarke
Chinese Art
James J. Lally, 472-3516
Chinese Paintings
Paula Gasparello, 472-3529

Coins
Dr. Jeremiah Brady, 472-4847
Contemporary Paintings, Drawings & Sculpture
Linda R. Silverman, 472-3543
English Furniture
Gerald Bland, 472-3513
European Furniture
Thierry Millerand, 472-3514
European & Chinese Export Porcelain
Letitia Roberts, 472-3517
European Works of Art, Ceramics & Tapestries
Armin Allen, 472-3506
Impressionist & Modern Paintings
John L. Tancock, 472-3547
Islamic Works of Art, Miniatures & Manuscripts
Michael Jones, 472-3524

Japanese Art
D. Martin Lorber, 472-3525
Jewelry
Dennis J. Scioli, 472-3421
Paul A. Russo, 472-3422
Modern Paintings & Sculpture
Shary E. Grossman
Polly Rubin, 472-3545
Modern Drawings; Ballet & Theatre Arts
Hermine Chivian-Cobb, 472-4764
Musical Instruments
Lauren Boucher, 472-8443
19th Century European Paintings
Judith Landrigan, 472-3537
19th & 20th Century Works of Art
Barbara E. Deisroth, 472-3508
Old Master Paintings
Brenda J. Auslander, 472-3541

Photographs
Anne Horton, 472-3595
Portrait Miniatures and Paperweights
Sarah D. Coffin, 472-3532
Pre-Columbian Art
Claudia Giangola, 472-3523
Prints (Old Master)
Marc E. Rosen, 472-3437
Prints (19th & 20th Century)
Ruth M. Ziegler, 472-3437
Susan F. Pinsky, 472-3438
Rugs and Carpets
Michael Grogan, 472-3451
Russian Art
Gerard Hill, 472-3619
Silver, Vertu, Watches
Kevin L. Tierney, 472-3531
Stamps
Andrew Levitt, (203) 743-4458
Vintage Vehicles
Chrys Landrigan, 472-3503

ADMINISTRATIVE DEPARTMENTS

Assistant Controller
Arnold Aratoon, 472-3682
Assistant Treasurer
H. Garth Dickey, 472-3467
Administrative Services
Barbara Fischer, 472-3640
Advertising & Catalogue Production
Harriet F. Walley, 472-3415
Appraisals
Samuel T. Blaisdell, 472-3452
Art Transport Service
Ann Cook, 472-3468

Bids and Sales Records
Roberta Louckx, 472-3450
Catalogue Subscription
Helen F. Wellner, 472-3414
Consignment Advisory Services
Annette Benda, 472-3419
Credit Manager
Lola Capel, 472-3461
Customer Advisory Service
Jane Wyeth, 472-3486
Decorative Arts Representative
Loraine Pack Liebmann, 472-3570
Fine Arts Representative
Ruth Freudman, 472-4873

Estates Division
Theodore N. Kaplan, Esq.,
472-3453
Exhibitions Decorator
Alfred Bristol, 472-3489
Facilities
Edward F. McGovern, 472-3491
Heirloom Discovery Day Coordinator
Chrys Landrigan, 472-3503
International Offices Liaison
Wathena Slaughter, 472-3460

Inventory Control, Decorative Arts
Olivia Murray, 472-3501
Inventory Control, Paintings
Andrea Kust, 472-3535
Institutional Services
Robert D. Schonfeld, 472-3452
Newsletter & Publications
Betsy Pinover, 472-8458
Personnel
Cheryl Lincoln, 472-3479
Press Inquiries
Elizabeth Robbins, 472-4840
Special Client Services
Eunice S. Carroll, 472-3440

SALES CONDUCTED BY

Peter C. Wilson, C.B.E.   John L. Marion   Edward Lee Cave   C. Hugh Hildesley   David J. Nash   Robert C. Woolley
John D. Block   James J. Lally   Andrew Levitt   Marc E. Rosen   Dennis J. Scioli   William W. Stahl
Eunice S. Carroll   Gerard J. Hill   Lorna C. Kelly   David N. Redden   Stuart Bennett

Admin 3/80

CONDITIONS OF SALE

This catalogue, as amended by any posted notices or oral announcements during the sale, is Sotheby Parke Bernet Inc.'s and the Consignor's entire agreement relative to the property listed herein. The following Conditions of Sale, the Terms of Guarantee and any glossary contained herein are the complete terms and conditions on which all property is offered for sale. The property will be offered by us as agent for the Consignor, unless the catalogue indicates otherwise.

1. The authenticity of the Authorship of property listed in the catalogue is guaranteed as stated in the Terms of Guarantee; except as provided therein all property is sold "as is" and neither we nor the Consignor make any warranties or representations of the correctness of the catalogue or other description of the physical condition, size, quality, rarity, importance, provenance, exhibitions, literature or historical relevance of the property and no statement anywhere shall be deemed such a warranty or representation. Prospective bidders should inspect the property before bidding to determine its condition, size and whether or not it has been repaired or restored. We and the Consignor make no representation or warranty as to whether the purchaser acquires any reproduction rights in the property.

2. A premium of 10% of the successful bid price will be added thereto and is payable by the purchase as part of the total purchase price.

3. We reserve the right to withdraw any property before sale.

4. Unless otherwise announced by the auctioneer, all bids are per lot as numbered in the catalogue.

5. We reserve the right to reject any bid. The highest bidder acknowledged by the auctioneer will be the purchaser. In the event of any dispute between bidders, or in the event of doubt on the part of us as to the validity of any bid, the auctioneer will have the final discretion either to determine the successful bidder or to reoffer and resell the article in dispute. If any dispute arises after the sale, our sale record is conclusive.

6. If the auctioneer decides that any opening bid is below the value of the article offered, he may reject the same and withdraw the article from sale, and if, having acknowledged an opening bid, he decides that any advance thereafter is insufficient, he may reject the advance.

7. On the fall of the auctioneer's hammer, title to the offered lot will pass to the highest bidder acknowledged by the auctioneer, subject to all the conditions set forth herein, and such bidder thereupon (a) assumes full risk and responsibility therefor, (b) will sign a confirmation of purchase thereof, and (c) will thereupon pay the full purchase price therefor or such part as we may require. We reserve the right to impose a late charge of 1½% per month on the total purchase price if payment is not made in accordance with all of the conditions set forth herein. All property must be removed from our premises by the purchaser at his expense not later than 3 business days following its sale and, if it is not so removed, a handling charge of 1% of the purchase price will be payable by the purchaser per month until its removal, with a minimum of 5% for any property not so removed within 60 days after the sale. If any applicable conditions herein are not complied with by the purchaser in addition to other remedies available to us and the Consignor by law, including without limitation the right to hold the purchaser liable for the total purchase price, we at our option may either (a) cancel the sale, retaining as liquidated damages all payments made by the purchaser or (b) resell the property at public auction, and the purchaser shall be liable for any deficiency, costs, including handling charges, the expenses of both sales, our commission on both sales at our regular rates, all other charges due hereunder and incidental damages. At our option, payment will not be deemed to have been made in full until we have collected funds represented by checks, or, in the case of bank or cashier's checks, we have confirmed their authenticity.

8. Lots marked with ■ immediately preceding the lot number are offered subject to a reserve, which is the confidential minimum price below which such lot will not be sold. We may implement such reserves by bidding on behalf of the Consignor. In certain instances, the Consignor may pay us less than the standard commission rate where a lot is "bought-in" to protect its reserve. Where the Consignor is indebted to or has a monetary guarantee from us, and in certain instances, we or our affiliated companies may have an interest in the offered lots and the proceeds therefrom other than our commissions, and may bid therefor to protect such interests.

9. Unless exempted by law, the purchaser will be required to pay the combined New York State and local taxes or any applicable compensating use tax of another state on the total purchase price. The rate of such combined tax is 8% in New York City and ranges from 4% to 8% elsewhere in New York State.

TERMS OF GUARANTEE

We guarantee the authenticity of Authorship of each lot contained in this catalogue on the terms and conditions set forth below.

1. Definition of Authorship

"Authorship" means the identity of the creator, the period, culture, source of origin of the property, as the case may be, as set forth in the **BOLD TYPE HEADING** of such catalogue entry.

2. Guarantee Coverage

Subject to the exclusions of (i) attributions of paintings, drawings or sculpture executed prior to 1870, and (ii) periods or dates of execution of the property, as explained in Paragraph 5 below, if within five (5) years from the date of the sale of any lot, the original purchaser of record tenders to us a purchased lot in the same condition as when sold through us and it is established that the identification of Authorship (as defined above) of such lot set forth in the **BOLD TYPE HEADING** of this catalogue description of such lot (as amended by any posted notices or oral announcements during the sale) is not substantially correct based on a fair reading of the catalogue including the terms of any Glossary contained herein, the sale of such lot will be rescinded and the original purchase price refunded.

3. Non-Assignability

It is specifically understood that the benefits of this Guarantee are not assignable and shall be applicable only to the original purchaser of the lot from us and not to the subsequent owners or others who have or may acquire an interest therein.

4. Sole Remedy

It is further specifically understood that the remedy set forth herein, namely the rescission of the sale and refund of the original purchase price paid for the lot, is exclusive and in lieu or any other remedy which might otherwise be available as a matter of law.

5. Exclusions

The Guarantee covers only the correctness of description of Authorship (as defined in 1 above) as identified in the **BOLD TYPE HEADING** of the catalogue item but does *not* extend to (i) the identity of the creator of painting, drawings and sculpture executed before 1870 unless these works are determined to be counterfeits, as this is a matter of current scholarly opinion which can change, (ii) the identification of the periods or dates of execution of the property which may be proven inaccurate by means of scientific processes not generally accepted for use until after publication of the catalogue, or (iii) titles or other identification of offered lots or descriptions of physical condition and size, quality, rarity, importance, provenance, exhibitions and literature of historical relevance, which information normally appears in lower case type below the **BOLD TYPE HEADING** identifying the Authorship. Although our best judgment is used in attributing paintings, drawings and sculpture created prior to 1870 through the appropriate use of glossary terms, and due care is taken to insure the correctness of the supplemental material which appears below the **BOLD TYPE HEADING** of each entry in the catalogue, the Guarantee does not extend to any possible errors or omissions therein.

REMOVAL OF PROPERTY

Unless different arrangements have been agreed upon, all purchases must be removed by the buyer by 5 p.m. on the third business day following the sale. Purchases not so removed will be subject to a handling charge to cover our costs. See paragraph 7 of the "Conditions of Sale."

Clients are advised that packing and handling of purchased lots by our employees are undertaken solely as a courtesy for the convenience of clients; and in the case of fragile articles, will be undertaken at our sole discretion.

Although we recommend the use of professional packers, books and small articles which are not fragile can be packed on our premises, and, at our sole discretion, can be sent by mail or other carrier for a nominal charge. Prints and drawings in glazed frames cannot be handled in this manner. Charges for packing, insurance, and freight are payable by the purchaser. For further information: Miss Ann Cook, (212) 472-3468.

CS 4/80

ADVICE TO PROSPECTIVE BUYERS AND SELLERS

STANDARD COMMISSION RATES

Our standard commission for selling fine art property at auction is 10% of the successful bid price of each lot sold for more than $500 and 15% of the successful bid price of each lot sold for $500 or less, in either case together with an amount equal to the 10% premium paid by the buyer as part of the total purchase price.

BIDDING

Successful bidders attending the auction are required to sign a bid confirmation card upon the fall of the hammer and will not be permitted to take delivery of purchases until their checks have cleared unless they have previously established credit or made payment arrangements. A premium equal to 10% of the successful bid price will be added thereto and is payable by the buyer as part of the total purchase price.

As a convenience to clients who cannot attend a sale in person, Sotheby Parke Bernet will, if so instructed, execute written 'order bids' on their behalf, without additional cost. Order bidders should use the 'Bid Form' provided in the catalogue and note the 'Advice to Order Bidders' printed on each form. Telephone bids must be confirmed in writing or by cable. Sotheby Parke Bernet will not be responsible for errors or failure to execute bids.

Lots are bought for order bidders at the lowest possible price (which may be below the order bid price) subject to other bids and reserves. For further information: Mrs. Roberta Louckx, (212) 472-3450.

CATALOGUES AND PRICE LISTS

Catalogues, prepared by the expert departments involved, are published for all auction sales. These may be purchased singly or by annual subscription.

Printed lists recording the prices of all lots sold are also available. Single copies are $2.00 each.

The *Sotheby Parke Bernet Newsletter,* which lists sales held in New York, London, Los Angeles and elsewhere, is available for $3.00 per year ($5.00 overseas).

Catalogue subscription rates include the price lists and the *Newsletter.*

Catalogues, price lists, and detailed information on subscriptions are available at the galleries or by writing to the Subscription Department. (Please specify sale number when ordering.) For further information: Mrs. Helen F. Wellner, (212) 472-3414.

INSPECTION OF PROPERTY, VISITS

Prospective sellers who wish advice and auction price estimations on their property should contact the appropriate department(s) or the consignment advisor, Miss Annette Benda, (212) 472-3419.

Photographs may be submitted or arrangements made to bring property to the galleries. The Decorative Arts Counter (4th floor, 980 Madison Avenue, open Monday-Friday, 10 am to 5 pm) provides a free inspection and auction price estimation service and coordinates with the various expert departments. *It is always advisable to telephone before coming in.*

Visits to advise clients and evaluate property can be arranged. The usual fees for such initial visits are:

Manhattan	$25.00
Other boroughs of New York City	$50.00
New York Metropolitan Area	$100.00
Elsewhere in North America	$250.00

Traveling expenses are extra and the fee is refundable in the event of consignment for sale by Sotheby Parke Bernet within one year from the date of the visit.

APPRAISALS

Appraisals may be done for insurance, estate, family division or other purposes (*excluding* gift tax).

Appraisal fees vary according to circumstances. Flat rates will be quoted based upon expert time involved, total appraised value, and costs of processing. Travel expenses are additional. Appraisals can be delivered within three weeks from the date of the appraisal visit.

A partial rebate of our fee will be made on any property subsequently consigned to us for sale within a year of our appraisal. Further information may be obtained from Miss Marjorie Crodelle, or Mr. Warren P. Weitman, Jr., (212) 472-3452.

CURRENCY CONVERSION DISPLAY BOARD

A currency conversion display board will be operated at certain sales for the convenience of bidders. Foreign currency amounts displayed on the board are approximations determined by reference to New York foreign exchange market rates in effect at the close of business on the last business day prior to the sale. We assume no responsibility for any errors or omissions in foreign or U.S. currency amounts shown. The total purchase price and applicable taxes are payable by purchasers, in accordance with the conditions of sale, in U.S. dollars, at our offices in New York.

IMPORTANT INFORMATION FOR PROSPECTIVE BIDDERS

Please note Paragraph 8 of the Conditions of Sale dealing with the subjects of "reserves" and our "interest in offered lots other than normal selling commissions." The following definitions of terms and explanations of policies on these subjects and the implementation thereof are provided for your information and guidance.

"RESERVE"

Definition: A "Reserve" is the confidential minimum price agreed between the seller and us, below which the lot will not be sold. On unsold lots, less than full commission may be paid.

Policy: All lots marked with ■ immediately preceding the lot number are being offered subject to a reserve. Our standard advice to sellers is that reserves be set at a percentage of the mean of the estimates, generally somewhat below the low estimate shown in the estimate sheet provided with this catalogue. In no case do we permit a reserve to exceed the high estimate shown in the estimate sheet. Unsold lots, i.e., those which do not meet their reserve, are omitted from the price lists issued following sales.

Implementation: We as agent for the seller protect reserves, that is, place bids during the auction if and when the highest outstanding bid at any time during the sale is below the reserve on the lot being offered.

"OWNED PROPERTY"

Definition: "Owned property" is property which, at the time it is offered for sale at auction, is owned solely or partially by us or an affiliate (and in the sale of which we are acting as a principal and not an agent).

Policy: The purchase of property by us for sale at auction is an insignificant part of our overall business. Direct purchases are only made at the request of a client and, in these cases, only after standard commission sales or guaranteed minimum price sales have been rejected by the client. Reserve prices of property owned by us are set on the same or a lower basis than property sold for other consignors, that is, reserves usually will be set below the low pre-sale estimates provided with this catalogue and in no case will they be higher than the low estimates. Any owned property which is unsold at the auction will be omitted from the price lists following the sale. All property owned by us will be identified in the catalogue as "Property of Sotheby Parke Bernet Inc." or a similar recognizable designation. In some cases, the prior source of property will be identified, e.g., "Property from the Estate of John Doe sold by order of the present owner Sotheby Parke Bernet Inc."

Implementation: Our representatives will make no bids on our behalf except to protect a reserve placed by us as owner. Bidding by us to protect reserves on property is effected in the same way as bidding to protect reserves on property consigned by an outside seller.

"BUYER'S PREMIUM"

A premium of 10% will be added to the successful bid price of all property sold by us, whether consigned to us or "owned property" as defined above, and whether picked up or delivered, and this premium is payable by all purchasers, whether dealers, institutions, private collectors, or others.

"EXPORTATION PERMITS"

Certain property sold at auction by Sotheby Parke Bernet Inc. may be subject to the provisions of the Endangered Species Act of 1973. In order to export these items, special licenses must be obtained from the Department of the Interior, U.S. Fish and Wildlife Service. There are no assurances that any such license can be obtained. Please contact the appropriate expert department if you have any questions.

AFTERNOON SESSION
Friday, June 6, 1980 at 2 p.m.
Catalogue Numbers 1 to 123

Plated

■ 1 PAIR OF SHEFFIELD PLATED TWO-LIGHT CANDELABRA, circa 1790, on circular bases with fluted borders, engraved with crests, fluted vase-shaped stems, the bell-shaped sconces decorated with stiff leaves, matching branches, reeded borders, detachable nozzles. *Height 17 inches (43.2 cm.)*

Silver

■ 2 SILVER SWEETMEAT BASKET, Crichton Bros., London, 1911, in early George III style, pierced with foliate scrolls between embossed lobes, the rim and foot cast with scrolls and flowers, matching openwork swing handle, minor tears in piercing, 10 ozs. *Length 7⅛ inches (18 cm.)*

■ 3 GEORGE III SILVER SUGAR BASKET, Hester Bateman, London, 1781, of vase shape, pierced and engraved with interlaced festoons, with beaded borders and swing handle, one repair to piercing, lacks liner, 5 ozs. 10 dwts. *Height 5¼ inches (13.3 cm.)*
Provenance
   Cushing Toppan, Cambridge, Mass.
   Sold Parke-Bernet Galleries, New York, October 3, 1958, lot 76 (one of two)
See illustration

■ 4 GEORGE III SILVER SUGAR BASKET, Hester Bateman, London, 1782, of similar form to the preceding, also pierced and engraved with festoons, beaded borders, 6 ozs. 5 dwts. excluding blue glass liner. *Height 5½ inches (14 cm.)*
Provenance
   Cushing Toppan, Cambridge, Mass.
   Sold Parke-Bernet Galleries, New York, October 3, 1958, lot 76 (one of two)
See illustration

■ 5 SIX GEORGE III SILVER DESSERT SPOONS, with later fluted bowls, the stems later pierced and bright-cut with ferns, comprising four *by Hester Bateman, London, 1786;* and two *by Thomas Wallis, London, 1797,* 5 ozs. Fitted case.

6   7

■ 6 GEORGE III SMALL SILVER SUGAR BASKET, Hester Bateman, London, 1784, of vase shape, pierced with scrollwork and arches and chased with laurel festoons, wavy gadroon rim, openwork swing handle, pierced pedestal foot, 2 ozs. 12 dwts. excluding blue glass liner. *Height overall 5 inches (12.7 cm.)*
See illustration

■ 7 GEORGE III SILVER WAITER, Hester Bateman, London, 1789, of plain circular form, the rim chased with a running band of husks below a beaded border, on three beaded panel feet, the base engraved with initials and date 1789, 7 ozs. 15 dwts. *Diameter 7 inches (17.8 cm.)*
Provenance
   Cushing Toppan, Cambridge, Mass.
See illustration

3   4

■ 8 **PAIR OF GEORGE III SILVER SALTS,** Hester Bateman, London, 1788, of shaped oval form, with straight sides, pierced and bright-cut with foliage, beaded rims, on pilaster supports, 3 ozs. 10 dwts. excluding one blue glass liner, the other lacking. *Length 3½ inches (8.9 cm.)*

■ 9 **GEORGE III SILVER WAITER,** Hester Bateman, London, 1784, of circular form, crested center, the border chased with a running band of husks between two bands of beading, on three claw and ball feet, 7 ozs. 15 dwts. *Diameter 7 inches (17.8 cm.)*
Provenance
Cushing Toppan, Cambridge, Mass.

■ 10 **THREE GEORGE III SILVER BUTTER SHELLS,** Hester Bateman, London, 1784 or 5, with deeply fluted shells, shaped handles engraved with later crests within a beaded border, raised on two whelk feet, *marks rubbed,* repairs, 9 ozs. 10 dwts. *Length 6 inches (15.2 cm.)*
Provenance
Cushing Toppan, Cambridge, Mass.
Sold Parke-Bernet Galleries, New York, October 4, 1958, lot 298

■ 11 **SET OF GEORGE III SILVER DESSERT FLAT-WARE,** Paul Storr, William Seaman and Crossley & Smith, London, 1810/11, Thread pattern, with plain terminals, comprising:
twelve dessert spoons
twelve dessert forks
twelve dessert knives
the knives *by Paul Storr,* 28 ozs. excluding knives. In fitted wood case. *36 pieces.*

■ 12 **PAIR OF GEORGE III SILVER OVAL MEAT DISHES,** Paul Storr, London, 1815, of oval form, the gadroon rims decorated with shells and foliage at intervals, and with larger shells at each end, the borders engraved twice with contemporary armorials, 178 ozs. *Length 20½ inches (52 cm.)*
The arms are those of Bolton impaling Littledale.
Exhibitions
Princeton, New Jersey, Princeton University Art Museum, "English Silver", 1966, catalogue number 58
Brooklyn, New York, The Brooklyn Museum, 1962–1980, and bearing the loan number L62.1.46 & 47
See illustration of one

13

■ **13 PAIR OF GEORGE III SILVER FOUR-LIGHT CANDELABRA, John Scofield, London, 1784,** on circular bases, engraved with crest and coronets, fluted vase-shaped stems and sconces, fluted scrolled arms emerging from leaves, gadroon borders, engraved with crests below a baron's coronet, detachable nozzles and flame finials, *marked on bases, branches, drip-pans, sconces and nozzles,* the bases wood-based but with scratch weights "81 ozs. 2 dwts. pair," the branches weighing 137 ozs. *Height 21 inches (53.4 cm.)*

Provenance
Sold Sotheby & Co., London, July 24, 1975, lot 206
A similar pair of candelabra by John Scofield, 1784/90 were sold Sotheby Parke Bernet, New York, February 7, 1980, lot 712
See illustration of one

■ 14 FIVE SILVER TABLESPOONS, comprising a pair of Queen Anne dognose spoons, *maker's mark S. over W., London, 1710,* the terminals initialed and showing traces of gilding; another engraved with interlaced cypher, *London, 1708;* and two Irish Tablespoons, *by John Pittar and Michael Homer, Dublin, 1776/78,* 10 ozs. 10 dwts.
Exhibitions
> The first two spoons, Brooklyn, New York, The Brooklyn Museum, 1962–1980, and bearing the loan numbers L62.1.10 & 11

■ 15 PAIR OF GEORGE III SILVER THREE-LIGHT CANDELABRA, John Green & Co., Sheffield, 1796/7, on circular bases, with vase-shaped stems and bell-shaped sconces, decorated with vertical lobes and reeded borders, fluted scrolled arms, detachable nozzles and ball finials, engraved with armorials and crests, *fully marked,* weighted. *Height 18½ inches (47 cm.)*
> The arms are those of Hodgson.
Exhibitions
> Brooklyn, New York, The Brooklyn Museum, 1963–1980, and bearing the loan numbers L63.13.26 a-j and L63.13.27 a-j
See illustration of one

■ 16 PAIR OF GEORGE III SILVER TABLE CANDLESTICKS, John Green & Co., Sheffield, 1796/7, *en suite* with the preceding and similarly engraved, weighted. *Height 12 inches (30.5 cm.)*
Exhibitions
> Brooklyn, New York, The Brooklyn Museum, 1963–1980, and bearing the loan numbers L63.13.14 a & b and L63.13.15 a & b
See illustration

16   15   16

17

■ **17 GEORGE III SILVER OVAL SALVER, Thomas Hannam and John Crouch, London, 1806**, with ovolo rim and fluted border, engraved with armorials on a drapery mantle within a border of anthemia, on four winged paw feet, 24 ozs. 12 dwts. *Length 11 inches (28 cm.)*

The arms are those of Cole impaling Cooke.

Exhibitions

Princeton, New Jersey, Princeton University Art Museum, "English Silver", 1966, catalogue number 57

Brooklyn, New York, The Brooklyn Museum, 1962–1980, and bearing the loan number L62.1.45

See illustration

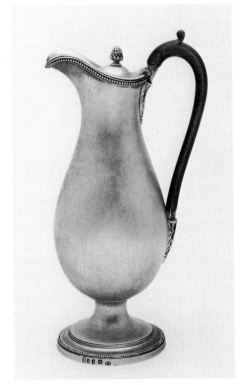

■ **18 GEORGE III SILVER HOT WATER JUG, John Scofield, London, 1786**, of pear shape with beaded borders and bud finial, the handle terminals chased with stiff leaves, *marked on foot and cover,* 24 ozs. 10 dwts. gross. *Height 10¾ inches (27.3 cm.)*

The arms are those of Frederick Robinson, 1st Baron Grantham and his wife Catherine Harris.

Exhibitions

Brooklyn, New York, The Brooklyn Museum, 1962–1980, and bearing the loan number L62.1.44

See illustration

18

19

■ 19 SET OF FOUR GEORGE II SILVER TABLE CANDLESTICKS, Simon LeSage, London, 1756, on shaped square bases, with deeply fluted baluster stems, campana-shaped sconces and detachable nozzles, decorated at intervals with leaves, bold gadroon borders, *marked on bases, sconces and nozzles, one base maker's mark and lion passant only,* 136 ozs. *Height 10⅝ inches (27 cm.)*

Provenance
    Sold Sotheby & Co., London, May 14, 1959, lot 91
Exhibitions
    Brooklyn, New York, The Brooklyn Museum, 1960–1980, and bearing the loan number L60.4.5 A, B, C, & D
See color illustration

■ **20 SET OF FOUR GEORGE II SILVER LARGE TABLE CANDLESTICKS, Eliza Godfrey, London, 1743,** on shaped circular bases chased with scrollwork, shells and flowers, the domed centers applied with shellwork, the incurved octagonal baluster stems rising from knops chased with interlaced ribbons enclosing flowerheads, decorated with overlapping shellwork, and rising to shoulders capped by leaves, campana-shaped sconces chased with stiff leaves alternating with shells and husks, with interlaced ribbonwork rims, detachable nozzles chased with shells and flowers, *marked on bases and sconces,* 124 ozs. *Height 10 inches (25.5 cm.)*
Provenance
    Sold Sotheby & Co., London, April 2, 1963, lot 32
Exhibitions
    Brooklyn, New York, The Brooklyn Museum, 1965–1980, and bearing the loan number L65.13.8 A, B, C, & D
See color illustration

21

■ **21 GEORGE II SILVER EPERGNE, William Cripps, London, 1757**, the central boat-shaped basket raised on an oval reel-shaped frame, both pierced with scrollwork, raised on four scroll feet with shell terminals, linked by openwork aprons of dragon-topped swags of flowers and shells, fitted, on leaf-decorated arms, with four candle sockets and four sweetmeat dishes, engraved with contemporary armorials, *marked on stand, basket, dishes and branches,* 156 ozs. 16 dwts. *Height 14¼ inches (36.2 cm.)*

The arms are probably those of Dyke of Horham, Sussex, probably for Anne Dyke, widow of Sir Thomas Dyke of Lullingstone Castle, co. Kent, who died in 1756

Exhibitions

Brooklyn, New York, The Brooklyn Museum, 1964–1980, and bearing the loan number L64.3.8

See illustration

22 (detail)

22

**■ 22 GEORGE II ROYAL SILVER CAKE BASKET,
George Wickes, London, 1743,** of shaped oval form, the
rim decorated with shellwork, floral sprays and overlapping
scales, swing handle decorated with dolphin heads, wave and
shell ornaments and rising from grotesque heads, the sides
pierced with diaper and scrollwork, the center engraved with
armorials, raised on four scroll feet headed by rococo cartouches containing facing harlequin heads, 59 ozs. 5 dwts.
Length 14¼ inches (36.2 cm.)

 The arms are those of Frederick-Lewis, Prince of Wales, b. 1707,
d. 1751.

 Research by Arthur Grimwade traces this basket to an entry in
Wickes' ledger, April 14, 1744.

"His Royal Highness the Prince of Wales, folio 140, April 14,
1744," among other items: "2 bread baskets—Lady Archibald
Hamilton—120 ozs. 12 dwts.—9s 2d per ounce—Total £55.5.7."The
notation in the ledger "Lady Archibald Hamilton" would indicate
that these baskets were presented by Prince Frederick to his mis-
tress, Lady Archibald Hamilton, upon her appointment as lady in
waiting to his mother, the Queen.

Provenance
 Mrs. Charles E. S. McCann
Exhibitions
 Princeton, New Jersey, Princeton University Art Museum,
  1966, catalogue number 48
 Brooklyn, New York, The Brooklyn Museum, 1956–1980,
  and bearing the loan number L60.2.9
See color illustration and black and white detail opposite

■ 23 **PAIR OF GEORGE II SILVER MUGS, Paul Crespin, London, 1740,** of tapered cylindrical form, with tuck-in bases and molded feet, flat-chased near the rim and below the handle with a band of rococo ornament, leaf-capped scroll handles, 15 ozs. *Height 3¾ inches (9.6 cm.)*
Provenance
   Sold Christie's, London, May 13, 1964, lot 110
Exhibitions
   Brooklyn, New York, The Brooklyn Museum, 1965–1980, and bearing the loan number L65.13.7 A & B
See illustration

23

Property of Mrs. Pearl D. Morrison

■ 24 **SUPERB GEORGE II SILVER LARGE RECTANGULAR TRAY, Paul de Lamerie, London, 1741,** the reeded rim with shell and foliate cartouches at intervals, the surface finely engraved with a band of scrolled strapwork, interrupted by cartouches, representing the Elements—
   No. 1.—*Water;* a dolphin surrounded by horse-form fountains, bullrushes and tridents
   No. 2.—*Air;* winged putto heads blowing air in a cartouche, surrounded by eagle wings, a bow and quiver
   No. 3.—*Fire;* a phoenix in a dragon-form cartouche
   No. 4.—*Earth;* a hart running by a tree backed by a trophy of hound and hunting motifs
all spaced by shellwork and sprays of corn and with crests in the angles, the center engraved with *accollé* armorials, surrounded by trophies of hunting, surmounted by an eagle with spread wings, grasping a snake, and terminated by a putto lying on a reed-covered shell, on four shaped bracket feet decorated with leaves on a trellis ground, 195 ozs. *Length 26 inches (66 cm.)*
   The arms are those of Child impaling Newport, and with, on separate shield, the arms of Jodrell.
Provenance
   Earl of Jersey
Exhibitions
   London, "Queen Charlotte's Loan Exhibition of Old Silver", 1929
   New York City, Parke-Bernet Galleries, "Art Treasures Exhibition", 1967
   Brooklyn, New York, The Brooklyn Museum, 1968–1980, and bearing the loan number L68.22.9
Literature
   P.A.S. Phillips, *Paul de Lamerie, His Life and Work,* p. 95, pl. LXXXVII
See color illustration and details on following page and dustjacket

24

24-1

24-3

24-2

24-4

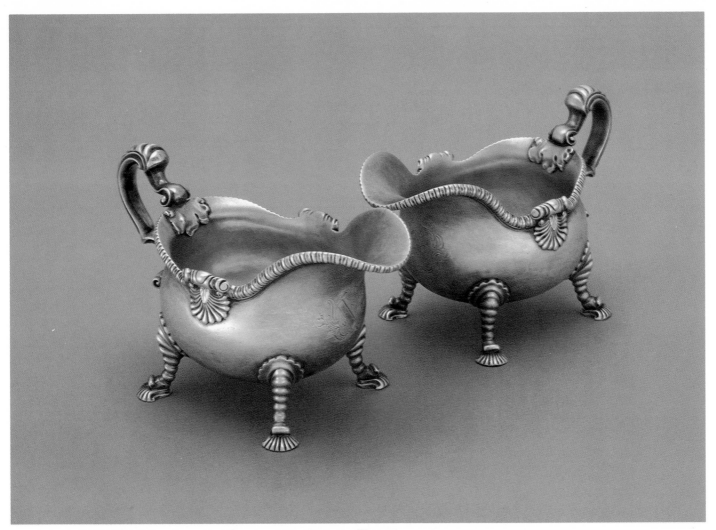

25

■ 25 **PAIR OF GEORGE II SILVER SAUCE BOATS,
Paul de Lamerie, London, 1742,** the waved gadroon rims
applied at the center with shells crested by scrolls, the fronts
engraved with contemporary armorials in rococo cartouches,
each raised on four knuckled scroll feet parting from scalloped ovals and terminating in shells, the knuckled and molded
triple scroll handles joined at the top by ragged leaves or
pelts and at the base by flowerheads, 45 ozs. *Length 9 inches
(22.8 cm.)*

The arms are those of Bright, Claybroke, co. Nothumberland
Provenance

Sold Sotheby Parke Bernet, New York, April 26, 1978, lot
801
See color illustration

■ **26 GEORGE II SILVER LARGE SALVER, Paul de Lamerie, London, 1743,** engraved with armorials in a rococo cartouche, the border cast and pierced with grapevine between male and female heads, on four pierced vine cluster feet, 146 ozs. 16 dwts. *Diameter 22 inches (55.8 cm.)*

The arms are those of Waldo, impaling Wakefield.

Provenance

Sir Timothy Waldo

E.G.B. Meade-Waldo

William Randolph Hearst

Bryant Jenks, Esq.

Sold Christie's, London, June 16, 1965, lot 32

Exhibitions

Princeton, New Jersey, Princeton University Art Museum, "English Silver", 1966, catalogue number 49

Brooklyn, New York, The Brooklyn Museum, 1966–1980, and bearing the loan number L66.18.9

Literature

For a similar salver, see P.A.S. Phillips, *Paul de Lamerie, His Life and Work,* p. 107, pl. CXXXVII

See color illustration opposite and black and white details

26 (detail)

■ 27 **PAIR OF GEORGE II SILVER SALVERS, Paul de Lamerie, London, 1745,** of shaped square form, raised on four scroll feet entwined with grapevine below overlapping shells, the raised border overlaid with trailing grapevine on a scalework ground, the surface flat-chased with grapevine over shell and scrollwork, the centers engraved with contemporary armorials, 71 ozs. 12 dwts. *Diameter 10 inches (25.4 cm.)*

The arms of those of Coote impaling Newport, for Algernon Coote, who succeeded his brother in 1720 as sixth Earl of Mountrath in Queens County, and his wife Diana whom he married in 1721, youngest daughter of Richard Newport, second Earl of Bradford. Algernon Coote M.P. for Castle Rising, 1724–34, and for Hedon at the age of 55.

Provenance
Sold Sotheby & Co., London, November 17, 1960, lot 153
Exhibitions
Princeton, New Jersey, Princeton University Art Museum, "English Silver", 1966, catalogue number 50
Brooklyn, New York, The Brooklyn Museum, 1962–1980, and bearing the loan number L62.1.29 & 30
Literature
W.D. John and Jacqueline Simcox *English Decorated Trays,* pp. 26–27
Michael Clayton, *Collector's Dictionary of the Silver and Gold of Great Britain and North America,* pl. 468
See color illustration

28

■ **28 GEORGE II SILVER LEMON STRAINER, Paul de Lamerie, London, 1742**, the circular bowl pierced in a formal flowerhead pattern, engraved with a crest and coronet, elongated openwork scroll handles of cartouche form terminating in shells and leaves, 5 ozs. 10 dwts. *Length 8⅛ inches (20.5 cm.)*
Exhibitions
   Brooklyn, New York, The Brooklyn Museum, 1974–1980, and bearing the loan number L74.10.3
See illustration

29 (detail)

■ **29 PAIR OF GEORGE II SILVER SAUCE BOATS
WITH A PAIR OF SAUCE LADLES, Paul de Lamerie,
London, 1740/42,** the sauce boats with bound reeded rims,
centered by scrolls above shells, applied below the lips with
shells and floral sprays and engraved with later armorials, leaf-
capped triple-scroll handles parting from shells, raised on
four lion mask and paw feet, the ladles with scrolled terminals, decorated with cherub heads, shells, grapevine and flowers, *the sauce boats 1740, the ladles 1742,* 52 ozs. 5 dwts.
Length 9⅛ inches (23.2 cm.)
    The arms are those of Parker, Baron Boringdon.

Provenance
    Sold Christie's, London, June 4, 1958, lot 153
Exhibitions
    Baltimore, Maryland, Baltimore Museum of Art, "The Age
    of Elegance: The rococo and its effect", 1959, catalogue
    number 382
    Princeton, New Jersey, Princeton University Art Museum,
    "English Silver", 1966, catalogue number 44
    Brooklyn, New York, The Brooklyn Museum, 1960–1980,
    and bearing the loan number L60.4.3 A, B, C & D
See color illustration and details of ladles on preceding page

■ 30 SET OF FOUR GEORGE II SILVER TABLE
CANDLESTICKS, Paul de Lamerie, London, 1739, on
square bases with incurved angles, chased with strapwork and
shells and applied with shells backed by crossed torches and
foliage sprays on matted and scalework ground, the baluster
stems chased with husk pendants, rising from knops chased
with paterae and roundels, the shoulders capped by shells,
the campana-shaped sconces chased with curled leaves alternating with scrolls, 75 ozs. 10 dwts. *Height 8 inches (20.3 cm.)*

The crest is that of Sir Michael Arthur Bass, created Baron Burton
in 1882, died in 1909 when the title became extinct.
A similar set of four candlesticks (1737–8) from the Swaythling
collection is described and illustrated in Phillips, *Paul de Lamerie,
His Life and Work,* p. 100, pl. LXI
Another set, possibly the same, is in the Francis Clark Art Insti-
tute, Williamstown, Massachusetts, also 1737–8.
Provenance
   Sold Sotheby Parke Bernet, New York, March 20, 1970,
   lot 247
   Sold Sotheby Parke Bernet, New York, June 4, 1974, lot
   76
See color illustration

NEC CUPIAS NEC METUAS

31

31 (detail)

■ 31 PAIR OF RARE GEORGE II SILVER LARGE SALVERS ON FOOT, Paul de Lamerie, London, 1736, in William III Style, the rim decorated with gadroons alternating with overlapping scales, and with an inner border of shells and scrolling strapwork on matted ground, engraved with contemporary armorials, raised on a screw-on pedestal base with gadroon border, surrounded by spreading cut-card work lightly engraved with scrolls, 170 ozs. *Diameter 16¼ inches (41.2 cm.)*

The arms are those of Philip Yorke, Attorney General, 1724 to 1733, Chief Justice, 1733 to 1737, and Lord Chancellor, 1737 to 1756. He was created Baron Hardwicke of Hardwicke co. Gloucester, in 1733, and in 1754 Earl of Hardwicke. A great lawyer and judge, he was constantly attacked by Walpole. He married in 1719 Margaret, daughter of Charles Cocks of Worcester, and died in 1764 at the age of 73.

Provenance
Mrs. John S. Phipps, Westbury, Long Island
Sold Sotheby & Co., London, February 20, 1964, lot 100
Exhibitions
Princeton, New Jersey, Princeton University Art Museum, "English Silver", 1966, catalogue number 39
Brooklyn, New York, The Brooklyn Museum, 1966–1980, and bearing the loan number L64.12.1 A & B
Literature
Connoisseur, May 1964, p. 63
The Ivory Hammer, Vol. II, p. 172
Auction Magazine, December 1971, p. 34
See color illustration opposite and detail of base of one

32

■ 32 GEORGE I SILVER-GILT CUP AND COVER,
Paul de Lamerie, London, 1724, Britannia Standard, the
bell-shaped bowl applied below the molded girdle with strapwork alternating with lobes and decorated with shells and
bearded masks, the domed cover similarly applied with strapwork decorated with female heads on matted grounds, leaf-
capped scroll handles, baluster finial pedestal foot flat-chased
with strapwork, *marked on base, body and cover,* 85 ozs. *Height
12 inches (30.5 cm.)*
Provenance
>Rt. Hon. Lady Islington
>Sold Christie's, London, June 19, 1957, lot 46

Exhibitions
>Princeton, New Jersey, Princeton University Art Museum,
>"English Silver", 1966, catalogue number 27
>Brooklyn, New York, The Brooklyn Museum, 1958–1980,
>and bearing the loan number L58.4.2 A & B

Literature
>*Antiques Magazine,* May 1964
>An identical cup by Lamerie, dated 1723, with the arms of
>the Hon. George Treby, is illustrated by J. F. Hayward,
>*Huguenot Silver in England,* pl. 8

See color illustration on following page

33

■ 33 GEORGE II SILVER HOT WATER JUG, **Chris-
tian Hillan, London, 1738,** of pear shape, chased with bands
of rococo ornament including shells pouring water and sprays
of flowers on matted and scrollwork ground, the short spout
molded and chased with a female mask, the cover chased with
spreading leaves, raised on three leaf-decorated shell and
scroll feet, ivory handle, *marked on base and cover,* 29 ozs.
gross. *Height 9½ inches (24.2 cm.)*
Provenance
>Edward Rice, Esq., Dane Court, Tilmanstone, Kent
>Sold Christie's, London, December 14, 1960, lot 169

Exhibitions
>Dallas-Fort Worth, Texas, Dallas-Fort Worth Art Center
>Museum, "One Hundred Years of English Silver," 1969
>Brooklyn, New York, The Brooklyn Museum, 1962–1980,
>and bearing the loan number L62.1.28

Literature
>*Connoisseur,* April 1964

See illustration

34

34 PAIR OF GEORGE II SILVER LARGE TABLE CANDLESTICKS, John Jacobs, London, 1739, of octagonal baluster form, chased with borders of strapwork, shells and foliage interrupted by full face and profile masks on matted grounds, molded borders, engraved with armorials, one with two angle splits, *marked on bases and sconces,* 50 ozs. *Height 9 inches (22.8 cm.)*
Provenance
    Walter P. Chrysler, Jr.
    Sold Parke-Bernet Galleries, New York, October 18, 1956, lot 91
Exhibitions
    Brooklyn, New York, The Brooklyn Museum, 1958–1980, and bearing the loan number L58.10.6 A & B
See illustration

35 GEORGE II IRISH SILVER QUATREFOIL SALVER, John Hamilton, Dublin, 1737, the rim chased with flowerheads enclosed by interlaced ribbons, with leaves at intervals, the surface flat-chased with a strapwork border enclosing vases of fruit, foliage and paterae on matted ground, the center engraved with contemporary armorials in an architectural cartouche flanked by winged demi-figures holding swags and terminated by a female mask, on four openwork and shaped bracket feet, 61 ozs. 7 ozs. *Width 15½ inches (39.4 cm.)*
    The arms are those of Burton quartering Campbell and impaling Ponsonby, for the Rt. Hon. Benjamin Burton of Burton Hall, co. Carlow, a Privy Councillor for Ireland, and his wife Anne, whom he married in 1734, daughter of Brabazon Ponsonby, first Earl of Bessborough.
Provenance
    Sold Sotheby & Co., London, July 9, 1964, lot 100
Exhibitions
    Princeton, New Jersey, Princeton University Art Museum, "English Silver", 1966, catalogue number 41
    Brooklyn, New York, The Brooklyn Museum, 1965–1980, and bearing the loan number L65.13.6
Literature
    Michael Clayton, *Collector's Dictionary of the Silver and Gold of Great Britain and North America,* pl. 465
See color illustration

35

36

■ 36 GEORGE II SILVER TAPERSTICK, William Gould, London, 1746, on shaped square base with fluted baluster stem, campana-shaped sconce, molded borders, 4 ozs. *Height 4½ inches (11.4 cm.)*
Exhibitions:
Brooklyn, New York, The Brooklyn Museum, 1963–1980, and bearing the loan number L63.13.20
See illustration

37

■ 37 GEORGE II SILVER TAPERSTICK, Jonathan Fossey, London, 1736, on hexagonal base engraved with a crest, with conforming baluster stem and banded campana-shaped sconce, molded borders, 3 ozs. *Height 4⅛ inches (10.5 cm.)*
Exhibitions
Brooklyn, New York, The Brooklyn Museum, 1963–1980, and bearing the loan number L63.13.11
See illustration

38

■ 38 GEORGE II SILVER TAPERSTICK, William Williams, London, 1745, on shaped square base, with partly faceted urn-shape stem and campana-shaped sconce, repair at base of stem, 4 ozs. 5 dwts. *Height 4¼ inches (10.8 cm.)*
Provenance
Walter P. Chrysler, Jr.
Sold Parke-Bernet Galleries, New York, October 18, lot 52
Exhibitions
Brooklyn, New York, The Brooklyn Museum, 1963–1980, and bearing the loan number L63.13.21
See illustration

39

■ **39 GEORGE I SILVER-GILT TAPERSTICK, Francis Turner, London,** 1726, of hexagonal baluster form with molded borders, the base initialed R.S., 3 ozs. 5 dwts. *Height 4⅜ inches (11.1 cm.)*
Exhibitions
 Brooklyn, New York, The Brooklyn Museum, 1963–1980, and bearing the loan number L63.13.7
See illustration on preceding page

41

40

■ **40 GEORGE I SILVER TAPERSTICK, J. Syngin, London,** 1716, on "umbrella"-shaped base with faceted baluster stem and fluted borders, 3 ozs. *Height 4½ inches (11.2 cm.)*
Provenance
 Sold Christie's, London, July 5, 1961, lot 158
Exhibitions
 Brooklyn, New York, The Brooklyn Museum, 1963–1980, and bearing the loan number L63.13.10
See illustration

■ **41 QUEEN ANNE SILVER TAPERSTICK, J. Laugton, Jr., London,** 1711, on octagonal base with circular well, urn-shaped stem, campana-shaped stem, gadroon borders, 3 ozs. 5 dwts. *Height 3⅝ inches (9.2 cm.)*
Provenance
 Sold Christie's, London, March 28, 1962, lot 149
Exhibitions
 Brooklyn, New York, The Brooklyn Museum, 1963–1980, and bearing the loan number L63.13.6
See illustration

■ **42 QUEEN ANNE SILVER TAPERSTICK, Richard Clarke, London,** 1708, on octagonal base, with central well, banded octagonal baluster stem and conforming sconce, 3 ozs. *Height 4¼ inches (10.8 cm.)*
Provenance
 Sold Sotheby & Co., London, May 12, 1966, lot 132
Exhibitions
 Brooklyn, New York, The Brooklyn Museum, 1968–1980, and bearing the loan number L68.22.2
See illustration

42

43

■ 43 GEORGE II SILVER LARGE CIRCULAR SAL-VER, Robert Abercromby, London, 1732, with molded "Chippendale" rim, on four leaf-decorated scroll feet, the center engraved with contemporary armorials in an architectural cartouche, flanked by female busts and eagles, surmounted by a shell and terminated by a winged grotesque mask, 101 ozs. *Diameter 18¼ inches (46.4 cm.)*

The arms are those of Fellows of Eggesford, co. Devon, and Shotesham Park, co. Norfolk, quartering Coulson.

Provenance
Mrs. M. Keim
Sold Sotheby & Co., London, December 14, 1961
Exhibitions
Princeton, New Jersey, Princeton University Art Museum, "English Silver", 1966, catalogue number 36
Brooklyn, New York, The Brooklyn Museum, 1965–1980, and bearing the loan number L65.13.5
Literature
W.D. John and Jacqueline Simcox, *English Decorated Trays*, pp. 14–15

See illustration

44

■ 44 **SET OF FOUR GEORGE II SILVER PEDESTAL SALTS**, David Willaume II, London, 1728, Britannia **Standard,** the shallow circular bowls applied with stiff leaves above a border of strapwork enclosing flowers, the pedestal bases chased with interlaced ribbonwork on matted ground, gilt interiors, the bases numbered 1 to 4 and with scratch weights, 31 ozs. 16 dwts. *Diameter 3 7/8 inches (9.8 cm.)*
Provenance
    Neville Hamwee, Esq.
    Sold Sotheby & Co., London, April 30, 1963, lot 20
Exhibitions
    Princeton, New Jersey, Princeton University Art Museum, "English Silver", 1966, catalogue number 33
    Brooklyn, New York, The Brooklyn Museum, 1964–1980, and bearing the loan number L64.3.4 A, B, C & D
Literature
    Antiques Magazine, May 1964
See illustration

45

■ 45 GEORGE I SILVER DISH, David Tanqueray, London, 1723, with scalloped molded border, fluted sides and rim foot, the center engraved with armorials within an architectural cartouche flanked by winged demi-putti holding husks, 10 ozs. 10 dwts. *Diameter 7 inches (17.8 cm.)*

The arms are those of Roberton, of Roberton-Earnook, Co. Lanark, Scotland.

Provenance

Sold Christie's, London, June 22, 1960, lot 14A

Exhibitions

Princeton, New Jersey, Princeton University Art Museum, "English Silver", 1966, catalogue number 25.

Brooklyn, New York, The Brooklyn Museum, 1962–1980, and bearing the loan number L62.1.19

See illustration

46

■ 46 **PAIR OF GEORGE II SILVER SAUCE BOATS,**
Anne Tanqueray, London, 1727, of *bombé* oval form, with
shaped molded rim, triple scroll handles, on four scroll feet
headed by faceted quatrefoils, engraved with a band of strap-
work, husks and paterae, 37 ozs. *Length 7 inches (17.8 cm.)*
Provenance
    Commander Edward Neville R.N.
    Sold Sotheby & Co., London, December 17, 1959, lot 137,
    illus. frontispiece
Exhibitions
    Brooklyn, New York, The Brooklyn Museum, 1960–1980,
    and bearing the loan number L60.4.2 A & B
Literature
    Compare with a pair of sauce boats by Lamerie, illus. P.A.S.
    Phillips, *Paul de Lamerie, His Life and Work,* pls. XLIX and
    L
    Michael Clayton, *The Collector's Dictionary of the Silver and*
    Gold of Great Britain and North America, pl. 474
See illustration

47

■ **47 GEORGE I SILVER TEA KETTLE ON LAMP-STAND, Thomas Gladwin, London, 1719,** of pear shape with molded borders, faceted swan-neck spout, wood swing handle, engraved with later armorials, the stand on three scroll feet and with hinged bail handle, *marked on base and cover of kettle, and base and cover of lamp,* 91 ozs. *Height 15¼ inches (38.7 cm.)*

The arms are those of Treby quartering Grange.

Provenance

Sold Christie's, London, April 15, 1964, lot 162.

Exhibitions

Brooklyn, New York, The Brooklyn Museum, 1964–1980, and bearing the loan number L64.12.7

See color illustrations

■ **48 TWO HISTORIC MATCHING GEORGE II SILVER SEAL-ENGRAVED SALVERS, Edward Vincent, London, 1728, and Maker's Mark I.L. mullet above, London, 1735**, each with "Bath" border, and raised on three unusual forked pear-shaped feet, each engraved in the center with representations of the seals of office given to Sir Robert Eyre by George II as Prince of Wales and King, surrounded by scrolling foliage and winged putti on reeded ground; the seals are as follows:

On the first: The Exchequer Seal of George II
Obverse: The King enthroned, flanked by figures of Britannia and Justice, and the Royal Supporters, beneath a baldachin surmounted by the Royal Arms
Reverse: The Royal Arms with dragon and greyhound supporters
Both bordered by Latin inscriptions and surmounted by The Royal Arms and terminated by the Arms of Eyre

On the second: The Seal of the Prince of Wales, subsequently George II
Obverse: The Prince enthroned, flanked by eagles and lions, badge and crest, and surmounted by his arms
Reverse: The Prince in Roman attire, with raised sword, mounted on horseback.
Both within the appropriate Latin inscriptions, surmounted by his arms and supporters and terminated by the arms of Eyre

83 ozs. 10 dwts. *Diameter 13½ inches (34.3 cm.)*
Both salvers are engraved below the Royal Seals with the Arms of Eyre, quartering Lucy and impaling Rudge, for Sir Robert Eyre of Newhouse, co. Wiltshire, Chancellor to the Prince of Wales, M.P. for Salisbury 1698–1710, and knighted in the latter year. He became Lord Chief Baron of the Exchequer in 1722 and Chief Justice of the Common Pleas in 1725. He married in 1694, Elizabeth, daughter of Edward Rudge of Warley Place in Essex and Abbey Manor, Evesham. Sir Robert was the eldest son of Sir Samuel Eyre of Newhouse, a Justice of the King's Bench in 1694, by Martha, third daughter and co-heir of Francis Lucy, fifth son of Sir Thomas Lucy of Charlicote, co. Warwick.

These form part of a small group of Seal salvers. It was customary for the Officer of State responsible for the seals of office to receive as a gift the matrix of obsolete seals and to have the metal fashioned into a silver object. At first it was customary to form these into cups, but at the end of the 17th century, it became the practice to make a salver on which the seal could be represented. Among those that survive are:
The Salver engraved with the Lord Chancellor's seal given to Charles Montagu, Earl of Halifax, and engraved by Simon Gribelin, circa 1695
A matching Salver made by David Willaume Junior, 1726
Two Salvers engraved with the seal of the Chancellor of the Irish Exchequer, made for Henry Boyle, 1702 and 1707, also engraved by Gribelin
The famous Salver engraved with The Great Seal, made by Lamerie, 1728, for Sir Robert Walpole and possibly engraved by William Hogarth
The Salver engraved with The Great Seal of Queen Caroline, by Henry Herbert, 1738, belonging to the Corporation of Kingston-upon-Thames
See J. F. Hayward, *Huguenot Silver in England,* for a discussion of Seal salvers, pp. 71–2. The engraving may be compared to the proof from the Gribelin-engraved salver, *op. cit.* p. 91B

Provenance
John Eyre Matcham, Esq.
Sold Sotheby & Co., London, June 10, 1965, lot 172
Exhibitions
Princeton, New Jersey, Princeton University Art Museum, "English Silver", 1966, catalogue number 34
Brooklyn, New York, The Brooklyn Museum, 1966–1980, and bearing the loan number L66.18.6 & 7
Literature
The Ivory Hammer 3, 1964–5, p. 210
See color illustrations on following pages

48

■ 49 PAIR OF QUEEN ANNE SILVER-GILT COV-
ERED BOWLS, Pierre Platel, London, circa 1710, applied
with strapwork in alternating formal and foliate designs on
matted ground, the domed cover similarly applied and with a
cast border of shells and leaves below the stylized bud finial,
gadroon rim and foot and beaded multiple scroll handles,
maker's mark only, struck twice on cover and base, 39 ozs. 7 dwts.
Diameter 4½ inches (11.4 cm.)
Provenance
   T. H. Cobb, Esq.
   Sold Christie's, London, October 9, 1957, lot 154

Exhibitions
   Princeton, New Jersey, Princeton University Art Museum,
   "English Silver", 1966, catalogue number 16.
   Brooklyn, New York, The Brooklyn Museum, 1958–1980,
   and bearing the loan number L58.4.5.6
Literature
   Antiques Magazine, May 1964
   Auction Magazine, December 1971, where it is noted that
   the bowls date from the period when Lamerie was appren-
   ticed to Platel and may therefore represent examples of
   Lamerie's early work.
See color illustration

50

■ 50 QUEEN ANNE SILVER CUP AND COVER, Jonah Clifton, London, 1709, with bell-shaped bowl and domed cover, both applied with cut-card foliage, engraved with contemporary armorials below an elaborate foliate mantle, the scroll handles capped by leaves and decorated with scalloped and ridged band, gadroon borders and urn-shaped finial, *fully marked,* 52 ozs. 10 dwts. *Height 9½ inches (24.2 cm.)*

The arms are those of Harrington.

Provenance
   Sold Christie's, London, December 1, 1960, lot 150
Exhibitions
   Princeton, New Jersey, Princeton University Art Museum, "English Silver", 1966, catalogue number 14.
   Brooklyn, New York, The Brooklyn Museum, 1964–1980, and bearing the loan number L64.3.1. A & B
Literature
   Antiques Magazine, May 1964
See color illustration

51   52   51

■ 51   PAIR OF WILLIAM AND MARY SILVER TABLE
CANDLESTICKS, Maker's Mark R.W. crowned, London,
1693, on octagonal bases, the urn-shaped stems applied with
lion masks at the angles, campana-shaped sconces, gadroon
borders, one base repaired, 32 ozs. *Height 6⅝ inches (16.8
cm.)*
Provenance
   Mrs. A. Hamilton Rice
   Sold Parke-Bernet Galleries, New York, May 6, 1965, lot
   121
Exhibitions
   Brooklyn, New York, The Brooklyn Museum, 1963–1980,
   and bearing the loan number L65.13.12 & 13
See illustration

■ 52   QUEEN ANNE SILVER LARGE CASTER, George
Garthorne, London, 1703, of cylindrical form, engraved
above a molded border with contemporary armorials within
a baroque cartouche, the high domed cover pierced and engraved with stylized urns of spreading foliage spaced by
fleurs-de-lys, the urn finial surrounded by spreading applied
strapwork in alternating designs, lobed borders, *marked on
body and cover,* 17 ozs. *Height 8¼ inches (21 cm.)*
   The arms are possibly those of Robinson.
Provenance
   Sold Christie's, London, April 25, 1960, lot 70
Exhibitions
   Brooklyn, New York, The Brooklyn Museum, 1962–1980,
   and bearing the loan number L62.1.7
See illustration

53

■ **53   WILLIAM III SILVER-GILT MONTEITH BOWL,**
Anthony Nelme, London, 1697, the sides vertically fluted
and with a matted collar, engraved with armorials in a baroque
cartouche surrounded by swags of fruit and enclosed within
an embossed cartouche of scrollwork on a pricked scalework
ground, with lion-mask and pendant bail handles centered by
ribbon-tied laurel, gadroon foot, detachable scalloped rim applied with putto masks and with matted borders, *fully marked*
on body, maker's mark on handles and rim, 92 ozs. 14 dwts.
Diameter 12 inches (30.5 cm.)

The arms are those of Cotton, for Sir Lynch Cotton (1701–1775)
who succeeded his brother as fourth Baronet of Combermere, co.
Chester, in 1748, and was M.P. of Denbighshire 1749 to 1774.
His grandson, Stapleton who led the famous cavalry charge at
Salamanca on July 22, 1812, when second in command under
Wellington, was created Viscount Combermere in 1827.

Provenance
   Lord Fairfax of Cameron
   Sold Sotheby & Co., London, November 17, 1960, lot 170.
Exhibitions
   Princeton, New Jersey, Princeton University Art Museum,
   "English Silver", 1966, catalogue number 9
   Brooklyn, New York, The Brooklyn Museum, 1962–1980,
   and bearing the loan number L62.1.6
Literature
   Antiques Magazine, May 1964
See color illustration

54

■ 54 QUEEN ANNE SILVER MONTEITH BOWL,
Robert Timbrell, London, 1704, the hemispherical bowl
chased with flutes outlined by matting and stamped with
flowerheads, handles pendant from lion masks, engraved with
crests within embossed baroque cartouches, detachable scalloped rim, applied with cherub heads and chased with shaped
matted borders, *marked on body and handles,* 57 ozs. *Diameter
11¾ inches (30 cm.)*
Provenance
    Sold Christie's, London, June 17, 1959, lot 106
Exhibitions
    Brooklyn, New York, The Brooklyn Museum, 1960–1980,
    and bearing the loan number L60.2.1
Literature
    For a similar monteith by Robert Timbrell, 1705, see Jack-
    son, *History of English Plate,* Vol. I, p. 278
See illustration

55   56   55

■ **55   PAIR OF WILLIAM AND MARY SILVER TABLE
CANDLESTICKS, Maker's Mark R.S.** with mullets in
quatrefoil, London, 1694, engraved with contemporary ar-
morials between crossed plumes, with stop-fluted stems and
gadroon borders, later weighted. *Height 9⅜ inches (23.7 cm.)*
Provenance
   Sold Sotheby & Co., London, January 18, 1962, lot 143
Exhibitions
   Brooklyn, New York, The Brooklyn Museum, 1963–1980,
   and bearing the loan number L63.13 2A & B
Literature
   Antiques Magazine, May 1964, p. 571
See illustration

■ **56   CHARLES II SILVER PATEN, Robert Cooper,**
London, 1682, with molded rim and recessed center, engraved with contemporary armorials, on reel-shaped foot, 11
ozs. 14 dwts. *Diameter 7⅜ inches (18.7 cm.)*
   The arms are those of Baron Morton, impaling Culme for Sir John
   Morton of Milborne, St. Andrew, and his wife, Elizabeth, daughter of Benjamin Culme, D.D. Dean of St. Patrick's, Dublin, and
   granddaughter of Sir Charles Pleydell.
   The paten and its matching chalice were donated by Baron Mor-
   ton in 1682 to the Parish Church of Milborne, St. Andrew, where
   they remained in service for 188 years, or until 1870 when they
   were presented to J.C. Mansel-Pleydell, Esq. in exchange for a new
   communion service, dated 1870.
Provenance
   Sold Christie's, London, January 17, 1964
Exhibitions
   Princeton, New Jersey, Princeton University Art Museum,
   "English Silver", 1966, catalogue number 5.
   Brooklyn, New York, The Brooklyn Museum, 1965–1980,
   and bearing the loan number L65.13.1
See illustration

57

Continental Silver

■ **57 DUTCH SILVER THREE PIECE TEA SET WITH SIMILAR TEA CADDY**, of oblong form chased with lobes, with reeded and corded borders and ball feet, comprising Teapot, Creamer and Sugar Basket with swing handle, *by H. F. Koen, Amsterdam, 1824, first standard;* and Caddy with hinged cover, lacks lock, *by I. Schalkwijk, Rotterdam, 1835,* 58 ozs. gross. *Height of teapot 5 inches (12.7 cm.)*
See illustration

Property from the Estate of Mabel Brady Garvan

■ **58 GERMAN SILVER BEAKER**, Jacob Bockelmann, Hamburg, circa 1690, of tapered cylindrical form, decorated with a broad band of granulation, engraved below the molded rim with a Judaic inscription, 6 ozs. 15 dwts. *Height 4⅝ inches (11.8 cm.)*
See illustration

58

59

■ 61 GROUP OF DUTCH SILVER MINIATURES,
comprising a Hanging Shelf, *maker's mark a bunch of grapes,
(cf. Citroen, no. 1066), late 17th century/early 18th century;* a
hexafoil Chamber Candlestick with pierced handle, *marks not
clear, late 17th century;* another with circular pan, *unmarked,
late 17th century;* a pierced Spatula, *maker's mark a stag, Haarlem, 1713;* a Tea Bowl and Saucer, *by Frederick van Strant I,
Amsterdam, circa 1720;* a fluted Tea Bowl and Saucer, *by Abraham Effemans, Amsterdam, circa 1730;* a Funnel and partly
chased Bowl, *both unmarked, early 18th century;* a Muffin Pan
by Johannes Adrianus van Geffen, Amsterdam, 1794; a Hearth
Brush *by Hendrik Duller, Amsterdam, 1807;* a Saucer, *maker's
mark only V.B.;* and a small Cup, *both 19th century. 14 pieces.*

■ 59 DUTCH SILVER BEAKER, Maker's Mark a crescent moon face, Nijmegen, 1615, of tapered cylindrical
form, lightly engraved with strapwork enclosing arabesques
which spread down the body, the molded foot stamped with
lozenges, the base engraved with initials A.C., 3 ozs. 15 dwts.
Height 4⅞ inches (11.8 cm.)
    For a similar beaker by the same maker also 1615, see Frederiks,
Dutch Silver, Vol. III, figure 140, page 47.
See illustration

**■ 60 DUTCH SILVER BEAKER, Maker's Mark H.R.
conjoined, Workum, date letter V., circa 1650,** of tapered
cylindrical form, engraved with strapwork enclosing scrolling
foliage and flowers from which hang fruit pendants alternating with lobate cartouches enclosing figures of Faith, Hope
and Charity, engraved near the base with birds perched on
sprays of berried foliage and a stork on a mound, the molded
foot with serrated leaf-tip border, stamped with lozenges and
applied with a cable band, the base engraved with a monogram and date 1652 surrounded by the inscription
EN•FOV•RINCKES*RINCKE•SANIS*, 5 ozs. 10 dwts.
Height 5 inches (12.7 cm.)
See illustration

60

63   64
62   65

■ **66 GROUP OF DUTCH SILVER MINIATURES,** comprising a realistically chased Basket *by Arnoldus van Geffen, Amsterdam, 1759;* a Tub with shaped raised handle and scalloped base, *by the same, 1761;* a Bed with four baluster feet, lacks headboard, *unmarked, 18th century;* a Washing Bowl on tripod stand; a Flat Iron with hinged top, *both 19th century;* a Trivet, *maker's mark a bunch of grapes, 18th century,* a Tea Kettle with swing handle, lacks cover, base repaired, *late 18th century;* a Cruet Bottle Holder from a basket-form cruet set and a Brandy Bowl with cast winged-figure handles in 17th century style. 10 *pieces.*

■ **67 GROUP OF DUTCH SILVER MINIATURES,** comprising a carcass stretched on a butcher's rack against a post, *maker's mark a stag, Haarlem, 1734;* a Music Stand on tripod base, *maker's mark ? a head, Amsterdam, mid-18th century,* top probably replaced; a tilt-top tripod Table, embossed with flowers and foliage, *Friesland, 19th century;* two porters carrying a barrel; and a horse and rider formerly attached to a cart, also *19th century,* 5 *pieces.*

68

■ **62 DUTCH MINIATURE SILVER SIDEBOARD DISH, Maker's Mark not clear, ? a head, Amsterdam, Late 17th Century/Early 18th Century,** the center lightly engraved with a patera, the wide border chased with putti emblematic of the Seasons in lobate cartouches, spaced by flowerheads. Together with another of hexafoil shape with fluted sides and domed center, *maker's mark only, Early 18th Century,* split rim. 2 *pieces. Diameter 3⅛ inches (8 cm.)*
See illustration of the first

■ **63 DUTCH MINIATURE SILVER DISH, Arnoldus van Geffen, Amsterdam, 1753,** of shaped oval form, engraved with a thread border at the rim, and with a star in the center. Together with a Cover, possibly of a tureen, in somewhat similar style. 2 *pieces. Length 4 inches (10.2 cm.)*
See illustration

■ **64 DUTCH MINIATURE SILVER SALVER ON FOOT, Maker's Mark not clear, ? a head, Amsterdam, Early 18th Century,** with punched beaded rim and short central capstan-shaped foot. *Diameter 2½ inches (6.3 cm.)*
See illustration

■ **65 DUTCH MINIATURE SIDEBOARD DISH, circa 1700,** with a wide border embossed with a running spray of flowers and foliage, *unmarked.* Together with two Dishes, the borders embossed with grapevine and acorns. 3 *pieces. Diameter 3½ inches (8.9 cm.)*
See illustration

■ **68 THREE CONTINENTAL SILVER WAFER BOXES,** of shallow circular form with leaf-tip rims and three bun feet, one pierced with a garland of flowers, *circa 1700,* another smaller pierced and engraved with St. John the Baptist, also *circa 1700,* the third engraved with the Agnus Dei, within rococo ornaments, *circa 1750.* Together with two filigree Boxes, the first, *early 18th century,* the second, *Mid-Eastern, probably circa 1800.* 5 *pieces. Diameters 2⅛ to 1¼ inches (5.4 to 3.2 cm.)*
See illustration

■ **69 MINIATURE SILVER TEAPOT, Continental, Early 19th Century,** of apple shape, engraved with festoons, loose cover, interlaced strap handle spreading from leaves and flowers, *unmarked.* Together with a pair of small baluster Ewers (possibly Altar Cruets), *unmarked, probably Italian, late 19th century* and an egg-shaped small Box, *maker's mark S.M. ?Samuel Moulton, London, Late 18th Century.* 4 *pieces. Height of teapot 3 inches (7.6 cm.)*

70

English and Irish Silver

■ **70 RARE GEORGE III SILVER MINIATURE TEA SET, Maker's Mark I.R., probably for John Reiley, London, 1818,** comprising Teapot, Coffee Pot, two-handled Sugar Bowl and Creamer, six Tea Cups, six Coffee Cups and six Saucers, of plain circular form, harp-shaped handles, the first four pieces with shaped gadroon borders, *fully marked,* 22 ozs. 10 dwts. *Height of coffee pot 4¼ inches (10.8 cm.)*
A miniature Tea Set complete with cups and saucers *maker's mark S.M., London, 1790,* was sold Sotheby Parke Bernet, New York, June 4, 1974, lot 73, illus.
See illustration

■ **71 SET OF TWELVE MINIATURE SILVER TEA-SPOONS AND MATCHING SUGAR TONGS, Early 19th Century,** plain Fiddle pattern, *unmarked.* 13 pieces.

■ **72 SILVER TWO-HANDLED CUP AND COVER, Crichton Bros., London, 1909, Britannia Standard,** in Queen Anne style, applied with strapwork and engraved with facsimile signatures, gadroon borders, the handles applied with *entrelac,* 117 ozs. *Height 15½ inches (39.4 cm.)*

■ **73 SET OF FOUR SILVER-GILT DESSERT DISHES,** of lobed and fluted circular form, applied in the center with armorials and surrounded by chased sprays of flowers, ribbon-tied reeded rim with grapevine at intervals, with shell and scroll handles, raised on four fluted scroll feet, *bearing marks for Butty & Dumee, London, 1769,* reshaped at a later date, 201 ozs. 10 dwts. *Length over handles 15¾ inches (40 cm.)*

■ **74 GEORGE III SILVER TEAPOT STAND, Thomas Ellerton & Richard Sibley I, London, 1803,** of oval form with straight gadroon rim, engraved with a monogram within a key pattern border, wood based. *Length 5½ inches (14 cm.)*

■ **75 GEORGE III SILVER COFFEE BIGGIN ON LAMPSTAND, Joseph Dodds, London, 1806,** of cylindrical form with short spout, acorn finial, and ivory handle, the lampstand with three reeded shell supports, straight gadroon borders, engraved with crests and motto, *marked on base and cover of biggin, on stand and lamp base,* 19 ozs. gross. *Height 9¼ inches (33.5 cm.)*

■ 76 GEORGE III SILVER MATCHING TEAPOT AND CREAMER, S. Hennell, London, 1800, of partly fluted almost spherical form, engraved with a collar of flowers and acorns spaced by ovals, scalloped rim, loose chained cover with beehive finial, *the creamer without maker's mark,* 21 ozs. gross. *Height of teapot 5 inches (12.7 cm.)*

■ 77 GEORGE III SILVER TEA KETTLE ON LAMP-STAND, Robert Sharp, London, 1790, of vase shape with reeded border, raffia-covered swing handle rising from acanthus, the lampstand with three reeded supports with hoof terminals surrounding a vase-shaped lamp and resting on a circular base with paneled feet, lacks cover, *fully marked,* 61 ozs. 10 dwts. gross. *Height 17¼ inches (44 cm.)*

■ 78 GEORGE III SILVER ARGYLE, Thomas Law, Sheffield, 1785, of vase shape, engraved with crest, loose domed cover with bud finial, central heating compartment with slip-on cover, repair at base of spout, *fully marked,* 8 ozs. *Height 6¾ inches (17.2 cm.)*

80

79

■ 79 GEORGE III IRISH SILVER DISH RING, William Townsend, Dublin, circa 1765, embossed with birds perched on swags of fruit and flowers and pierced with diaper and scrolls, 19 ozs. 10 dwts. *Diameter 7½ inches (19 cm.) at rim*
See illustration

■ 80 GEORGE III IRISH SILVER DISH RING, Charles Mullen, Dublin, 1771, pieced and chased with scenes from Aesop's Fables of The Fox and the Crow and the Fox and the Crane, a pair of birds and a hound with trophy in mouth, surrounded by buildings and flowers within crossed reeds, shellwork borders, 10 ozs. *Diameter 7⅛ inches (18 cm.) at rim.*
See illustration

■ 81 GEORGE III IRISH SILVER CREAMER, Matthew West, Dublin, circa 1760, of helmet shape with waved rim, molded girdle and three lion mask and paw feet, small repair to base, 8 ozs. 15 dwts. *Height 5½ inches (13.4 cm.)*
See illustration

■ 82 SET OF FOUR GEORGE II SILVER SALTS, Maker's Mark only W.C., circa 1750, circular with lion mask and paw feet and corded rims, *maker's mark struck three times on each salt,* 22 ozs. *Diameter 2⅞ inches (7.4 cm.)*
See illustration of two

82   81   82

83

■ **83   SET OF FOUR GEORGE II IRISH SILVER CAR-YATID TABLE CANDLESTICKS,** William Homer, Dublin, circa 1755, on shaped circular bases decorated with gadroons, flowersprays and shellwork, the stems in the form of demi-female figures holding sconces above their heads, detachable nozzles chased to match, one repaired at base of stem, *marked on bases, sconces and nozzles,* 111 ozs. *Height 10½ inches (26.6 cm.)*
See color illustration

84

■ **84 PAIR OF GEORGE II SILVER CARYATID TABLE CANDLESTICKS, William Cripps, London, 1752,** similar to the preceding, chased with flowers and shellwork, the bodies draped with garlands of flowers, detachable nozzles, *marked on bases and sconces,* 61 ozs. 10 dwts. *Height 11 inches (27.9 cm.)*
See illustration

■ **85 GEORGE III IRISH SILVER BOWL, Dublin, circa 1765,** of fluted hemispherical form, chased with pendants of flowers, fruit, dolphin spewing water and a bird, on lion mask and paw feet, rim splits, *maker's mark not clear,* 6 ozs. *Diameter 5⅛ inches (13 cm.)*
See illustration

85

■ **86 GEORGE III IRISH SILVER BOWL,** Matthew West, Dublin, 1762, later chased with sprays of flowers, on three shell-and-hoof feet, 5 ozs. 15 dwts. *Diameter 5½ inches (14 cm.)*

■ **87 GEORGE III IRISH SILVER BOWL,** Dublin, circa 1770, decorated probably at a later date with spiralled punched beading and flutes, lion mask and paw feet, *marks not clear,* 9 ozs. *Diameter 5¾ inches (14.5 cm.)*

90

■ **91 GEORGE II IRISH SILVER BOWL,** Dublin, circa 1755, with fluted sides and scalloped rim, raised on three lion mask and paw feet, *maker's mark not clear, but probably by John or Matthew West,* splits, 6 ozs. *Diameter 5¾ inches (14.6 cm.)*

■ **92 GEORGE III IRISH SILVER BOWL,** Matthew West, Dublin, 1788, decorated with spiralled punched beaded borders and with beaded rim, on three shell and hoof feet, engraved with crest below an earl's coronet, repairs, rim split, 5 ozs. 10 dwts. *Diameter 5¼ inches (13.2 cm.)*

■ **93 GEORGE II IRISH SILVER BOWL,** Robert Glanville, Dublin, circa 1755, with fluted sides and scalloped rim, engraved with a crest and raised on three lion mask and paw feet, repairs to flutes at rim, 5 ozs. 15 dwts. *Diameter 5¼ inches (13.2 cm.)*
See illustration

88

■ **88 GEORGE III IRISH SILVER BOWL, Probably by** Charles Townsend, Dublin, circa 1765, chased with birds and buildings, on three shell-and-hoof feet, repairs to rim, 6 ozs. *Diameter 5⅝ inches (13.4 cm.)*
See illustration

■ **89 GEORGE III IRISH SILVER BOWL,** Dublin, circa 1765, of fluted circular form, embossed with a dolphin, demi-lion, bird, shells and pendants of fruits and flowers, on three lion mask and paw feet, rim restored, *apparently no maker's mark,* 7 ozs. *Diameter 4⅞ inches (12.5 cm.)*

■ **90 GEORGE III IRISH SILVER BOWL,** Matthew West, Dublin, 1765, plain with punch-beaded rim, on three shell-and-hoof feet, 6 ozs. 10 dwts. *Diameter 5⅜ inches (13.7 cm.)*
See illustration

93

■ 94 SET OF FOUR GEORGE II IRISH SILVER TABLE CANDLESTICKS, John Moore, Dublin, 1752, on circular bases, tapered cylindrical stems and lobed shoulders, all chased with borders of overlapping foliage, *marked on bases and sconces, lack date letter but with Hibernia used for the year 1752,* 68 ozs. *Height 8½ inches (21.6 cm.)*
See illustration

■ 95 GEORGE II SILVER CASTER, Samuel Wood, London, 1747, of baluster form with molded borders, the cover cast and chased with sloping panels of scrolls and foliage, *marked on base and cover,* 5 ozs. 10 dwts. *Height 6 inches (15.2 cm.)*

■ 96 GEORGE II SILVER CASTER, Samuel Wood, London, 1747, of baluster form with molded borders, pierced and engraved cover with urn finial, piercing damaged, *marked on base and cover, the latter with different version of maker's mark,* 5 ozs. 5 dwts. *Height 6 inches (15.2 cm.)*

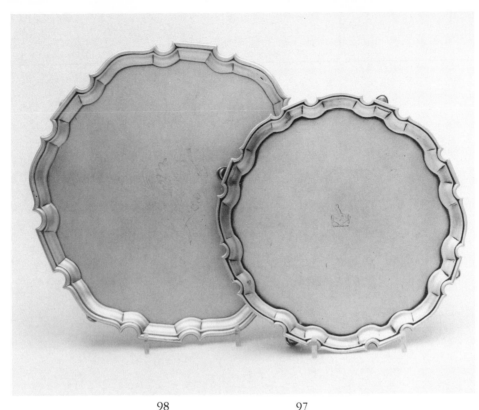

98   97

■ 97   GEORGE II SILVER CIRCULAR SALVER, Francis Spilsbury, London, 1738, with "Chippendale" rim and crested center, on three hoof feet, minor rim splits, 19 ozs. *Diameter 10 inches (25.4 cm.)*
See illustration

■ 98   GEORGE II SILVER CIRCULAR SALVER, Joseph Sanders, London, 1735, with shaped molded rim showing traces of engraved armorials, the back with inscription "The Countess of Portland's Legacy, 1751", small rim split, 30 ozs. *Diameter 12⅜ inches (31.4 cm.)*
    The arms are probably those of Egerton. The inscription presumably refers to Lady Margaret Cavendish Harley, only daughter and heir of Edward, 2nd Earl of Oxford, who married William, 2nd Duke of Portland in 1734. She was celebrated by Prior as "My noble, lovely little Peggy" (Burke's *Peerage,* 1894)
See illustration

■ 99   GEORGE II SILVER WAITER, Robert Abercromby, London, 1737, with "Chippendale" rim, the center engraved with armorials, on three hoof feet, rim split, 6 ozs. *Diameter 6 inches (15.2 cm.)*

■ 100   PAIR OF GEORGE II SILVER SALTS, John Wood, London, 1736, of plain circular form with three hoof feet, *marks rubbed.* Together with two other similar, *marks rubbed, London, 1759/68,* 10 ozs. *4 pieces. Diameter 2⅛ inches (7.4 cm.)*

■ 101   PAIR OF GEORGE I SILVER CASTERS, Starling Wilford or Samuel Welder, London, 1725, of vase shape, covers pierced and engraved with formal foliage, one repaired at base, *marked on bases and covers, one date letter obscured by solder,* 9 ozs. 10 dwts. *Height 5½ inches (14 cm.)*

■ 102   GEORGE II SILVER SALVER, Joseph Sanders, London, 1736, with molded "Chippendale" rim, plain surface, on four hoof feet, 28 ozs. *Diameter 12⅛ inches (31 cm.)*

103

■ 103 GEORGE II IRISH SILVER LARGE TWO-HANDLED CUP WITH A COVER TO FIT, William Homer, Dublin, circa 1740, of bell shape, engraved with armorials and chased with a band of strapwork enclosing engraved heads, bold leaf-capped scroll handles chased to match; the cover chased with a band of shell and scrollwork and with bud finial, *by John Walker, circa 1750,* one side patched, 127 ozs. 10 dwts. *Height 15 inches (38.2 cm.)*

The arms are those of Lowndes quartering Gorst for Lowndes of Palterton, co. Derby.
See illustration

■ 104 PAIR OF GEORGE II SILVER TWO-LIGHT CANDELABRA, Paul de Lamerie, 1745/47, of rococo baluster form, chased with flowers, shells and scrollwork on partly matted grounds, branches similarly decorated and with flaming urn finials, *marked on bases (one date letter invisible) and on sleeves of branches,* one repaired at base of stem, 100 ozs. 5 dwts. *Height 15¼ inches (38.7 cm.)*
See color illustration opposite

105

■ **105 GEORGE II SILVER TEA KETTLE ON LAMP-STAND**, Paul de Lamerie, London, 1729, Britannia Standard, of almost spherical form engraved with armorials and a border of strapwork, swing handle, matching stand with pierced and engraved gallery, fixed lamp engraved with the same armorials, three engraved shell feet, engraving worn, small repair to side of lamp, *marked on base and cover of kettle and base and cover of lamp,* 48 ozs. 10 dwts. gross. *Height 11½ inches (29.2 cm.)*
See illustration

■ **106 GEORGE II SILVER CUP AND COVER,** Paul de Lamerie, London, 1720, Britannia Standard, with plain bell-shaped body engraved with contemporary and later armorials, heavy scroll handles, molded pedestal foot, domed cover engraved with the same armorials, with baluster finial, *cover unmarked but probably original,* small split in cover, 54 ozs. 15 dwts. *Height 10 inches (25.5 cm.)*
   The first armorials are those of Belhouse or Chudleigh impaling Garnier. The later armorials, circa 1790, are those of Bayly impaling Addison.
See color illustration opposite

■ 107   **GEORGE I LARGE SILVER CASTER, Paul de Lamerie, London, 1719,** of vase shape engraved with contemporary armorials in baroque cartouche flanked by demi-figures holding swags, applied at the base with leaves, the cover pierced with strapwork and scalework, *marked on base and cover,* 18 ozs. 5 dwts. *Height 8½ inches (21.6 cm.)*

The arms are those of Brougham of Brougham, Westmorland quartering Vaux of Catterlen, Vaux of Trymane, and Delamore, later created (1830) Lord Brougham and Vaux.

For a similar caster by Lamerie, also 1719, see P.A.S. Phillips, *Paul de Lamerie, His Life and Work,* fig. X.

See color illustration

108

■ 108   GEORGE II IRISH SILVER TOILET BOX, William Sutton, Dublin, 1734, of straight-sided oval form, the hinged cover engraved with armorials in an elaborate baroque cartouche, with molded borders and four quadrangular baluster feet, *marked on body and cover,* 20 ozs. *Length 7 inches (17.8 cm.)*

The arms are those of St. George, Woodsgift, co. Kilkenny. *See illustration*

109

■ 109 PAIR OF GEORGE I IRISH SILVER SMALL
SALVERS ON FOOT, Thomas Sutton, Dublin, 1717,
with molded rims, crested centers and capstan bases, *marked
on salvers and feet,* 11 ozs. 5 dwts. *Diameter 5⅜ inches*
See illustration

■ 111 GEORGE I IRISH SILVER TWO-HANDLED
CUP, Joseph Walker, Dublin, 1715, the bell-shaped body
engraved with contemporary armorials and crest above a
molded girdle, leaf-chased harp-shaped handles, small split in
rim, minor repair behind cartouche, 26 ozs. *Height 6½ inches
(16.5 cm.)*
See illustration

110

111

■ 110 GEORGE II IRISH SILVER SALVER ON FOOT,
William Williamson, Dublin, 1729, circular with molded
rim, the center engraved with contemporary armorials, cap-
stan foot, repaired, *marked on salver and foot,* 18 ozs. 15 dwts.
Diameter 10¼ inches (26 cm.)
   The arms are possibly those of Nevill or Nevile.
See illustration

112   113   112

■ **112 PAIR OF QUEEN ANNE IRISH SILVER OC-TAGONAL TABLE CANDLESTICKS, Edward Work-man, Dublin, 1708–9,** of octagonal baluster form with molded borders, engraved with interlaced cyphers, *marked on bases and sconces,* small split in one base, 19 ozs. 15 dwts. *Height 5¼ inches (13.4 cm.)*
See illustration

■ **113 RARE GEORGE I SILVER TABLE BELL, Maker's Mark not clear, Possibly by Charles Laughton I, London, 1714,** with molded borders, surmounted by a seated putto, 6 ozs. 10 dwts. *Height 4 inches (10.2 cm.)*
See illustration

■ **114 GEORGE I SILVER BOWL, Joseph Clare, London, 1719,** of plain hemispherical form, with molded rim and foot, rim split, 5 ozs. *Diameter 4½ inches (11.4 cm.)*

■ 115 QUEEN ANNE SILVER CHOCOLATE POT,
Gabriel Sleath, London, 1711, of tapered cylindrical form,
engraved with contemporary armorials in baroque cartouche
flanked by perched birds, dome cover with hinged baluster
finial and chained hinge peg, the swan-neck spout with hinged
cover, split in base rim, pin in hinge of finial lacking, *marked
on base and cover,* 27 ozs. gross. *Height 10¼ inches (26 cm.)*
See illustration

■ **116 PAIR OF WILLIAM AND MARY IRISH SILVER SALVERS ON FOOT, Joseph Walker, Dublin, 1696,** with embossed gadroon rims and matching capstan bases, later engraved with armorials, one with an added strengthening rim inside foot, *marked on salvers and feet,* 27 ozs. *Diameter 9⅜ inches (23.8 cm.)*
See illustration

■ **117 WILLIAM AND MARY SILVER SALVER ON FOOT, Maker's Mark I.S., London, ?1692,** with embossed gadroon rim, the center engraved with armorials in a rococo cartouche *circa 1760,* capstan foot, repairs to rim, 28 ozs. 10 dwts. *Diameter 12¾ inches (32.4 cm.)*
 The Arms are those of Bunbery.

■ **118 SILVER WRITING SET, Maker's Mark I.C. pellet below in heart-shaped shield, Third Quarter 17th Century,** formed as a cluster of three cylinders to hold pens with a slip-on cap and a screw-on ink compartment, with an additional screw thread, presumably for a sand or seal compartment, molded borders, *maker's mark struck four times,* damage to borders, 1 oz. 15 dwts. *Length 6 inches (15.2 cm.)*

119

■ **119 EARLY CHARLES II SILVER CAUDLE CUP AND COVER, Maker's Mark R.F. between pellets (Jackson p. 127), London, 1660,** of pear shape, *repoussé* and chased with emblematic standing putti in lobate cartouches, surrounded by flowers, caryatid scroll handles, leaf-chased baluster finial, the cover with similar seated putti, emblematic of the Seasons, winter repeated, showing traces of pricked initials, several small repairs and holes, *marked on base and cover, 31 ozs. Height 8 inches (20.3 cm.)*

   Jackson records this maker for a caudle cup and cover, also 1660, in the possession of Crichton Bros.

See illustration

120

■ **120 CHARLES II SILVER CAUDLE CUP AND COVER, Maker's Mark S.B. trefoil below (Jackson p. 133), London, 1663,** of pear shape, embossed and chased with large flowers, fruit and foliage, caryatid scroll handles, paten-form cover with flat reel-shaped finial, slight split at top of one handle, cover with rim split and old repairs, *marked on body and cover,* 28 ozs. 10 dwts. *Height 6½ inches (16.4 cm.) See illustration*

■ **122 JAMES I SILVER BEAKER, Maker's Mark H.M.** conjoined with mullet below in shaped shield (cf. Jackson, p. 113), London, 1609, of tapered cylindrical form, engraved with pendants of scrolling foliage incorporating emblematic thistle, rose, acorn and pomegranate, which spread from a band of interlaced strapwork, the molded foot die-stamped with a band of linked circles enclosing beads, pricked with initials C.S. on the side and on the base with traces of initials $_{WA}^{C}$, 6 ozs. 10 dwts. *Height 5⅜ inches (13.7 cm.)* *See illustration*

121

122

■ **121 CHARLES II SILVER WINE CUP, Maker's Mark S.M.,** mullet below in heart-shaped shield, London, 1667, of slightly tapered cylindrical form, chased with vertical panels enclosing stylized acanthus leaves on matted ground within punched borders, raised on trumpet foot decorated with granulated band, the interior embossed with a flowerhead, the rim pricked with initials $_{DB}^{ST}$, flanked by the date 1669, *marked on cup and foot,* small split in rim, 3 ozs. 5 dwts. *Height 3⅞ inches (9.8 cm.)* *See illustration*

123

■ **123 ELIZABETH I SILVER BEAKER, Maker's Mark R.S. above a device, (cf. mark of Robert Signell, Jackson p. 105), London, 1599,** of tapered cylindrical form, engraved at the rim with strapwork enclosing scrolling foliage which spreads down the body into three sprays of flowers, enclosed by leaf-capped scrolls, the molded foot die-stamped with an upper band, of interlaced ribbons enclosing ovals and a lower band of ovolos, the body lightly pricked with series of later initials, and the date 1648, the base also pricked with initials, 7 ozs. 15 dwts. *Height 5⅞ inches (15 cm.)*
See illustration

END OF SALE

Sotheby Parke Bernet Inc.

980 Madison Avenue, New York, N.Y. 10021
Telephone 212 472-3435, 3436, 3450

Estimates (U.S. $)

GARVAN & MORRISON IMPORTANT SILVER
SALE 4390 • FRIDAY • JUNE 6, 1980.

NOTE: As a convenience to its clients, Sotheby Parke Bernet Inc. furnishes pre-sale estimates for all property included in the auctions. These estimates are our approximate valuations based, whenever possible, on comparable auction values excluding the 10% premium.

As provided for in the "Conditions of Sale" and as explained in the "Important Information For Prospective Bidders", all the property should be assumed to have reserves. In no case, where a reserve exists, will it exceed the range of estimates quoted below. **A buyer's premium of 10% will be added to the successful bid price of each lot sold.**

1	$1000/1500	38	$800/1200	75	$600/700	112	$8000/10000
2	300/400	39	1200/1500	76	900/1100	113	5500/6500
3	600/800	40	1500/2000	77	1400/1600	114	600/800
4	700/900	41	1200/1500	78	700/800	115	10000/12000
5	300/400	42	1200/1500	79	1800/2200	116	3500/4500
6	600/700	43	10000/12000	80	1500/2000	117	2000/3000
7	700/800	44	6000/8000	81	700/900	118	500/700
8	400/500	45	3000/3500	82	800/1200	119	6000/8000
9	600/700	46	5000/7000	83	8000/12000	120	5500/6500
10	900/1200	47	6000/7000	84	5000/6000	121	2000/2500
11	2000/2500	48	40000/60000	85	600/800	122	12000/18000
12	12000/14000	49	20000/30000	86	500/600	123	15000/20000
13	20000/25000	50	7000/9000	87	500/600		
14	550/650	51	6000/8000	88	600/800		
15	3000/3500	52	10000/12000	89	400/500		
16	1400/1800	53	16000/18000	90	700/900		
17	1800/2200	54	6000/8000	91	600/700		
18	2000/2500	55	6000/8000	92	500/600		
19	12000/15000	56	3000/4000	93	650/750		
20	15000/17000	57	1200/1500	94	7000/9000		
21	12000/15000	58	2500/3000	95	500/600		
22	16000/20000	59	8000/12000	96	250/300		
23	2500/3000	60	7000/9000	97	800/1000		
24	refer department	61	700/900	98	1000/1200		
25	30000/40000	62	300/400	99	300/400		
26	35000/45000	63	200/300	100	400/500		
27	40000/50000	64	200/300	101	900/1100		
28	5000/6000	65	150/200	102	1000/1200		
29	30000/40000	66	300/400	103	3000/4000		
30	60000/80000	67	400/500	104	30000/35000		
31	60000/70000	68	400/600	105	8000/10000		
32	25000/30000	69	300/350	106	7000/9000		
33	6000/7000	70	4000/5000	107	18000/22000		
34	10000/12000	71	200/250	108	4000/5000		
35	20000/25000	72	3000/3500	109	1500/2000		
36	900/1200	73	4000/6000	110	1200/1500		
37	800/1200	74	200/250	111	2000/3000		

Sotheby Parke Bernet Group Limited

Peter C. Wilson C.B.E., Chairman
The Earl of Westmorland, K.C.V.O., Deputy Chairman

AUCTION ROOMS AND REPRESENTATIVES* OUTSIDE NORTH AMERICA

UNITED KINGDOM

London

Sotheby Parke Bernet & Co.
34-35 New Bond Street
London W1A2AA
Telephone: (01) 493 8080
Telex: 24454 SPBLONG
Telegrams: Abinitio, London, W1

Sotheby's Belgravia
19 Motcomb Street
London SW1X 8LB
Telephone: (01) 235 4311
Telex: 24454 SPBLONG
Telegrams: Gavel, London

Sotheby Parke Bernet & Co.
(Hodgson's Rooms)
115 Chancery Lane
London WC2A 1PX
Telephone: (01) 405 7238
Telex: 24454 SPBLONG
Telegrams: Bookhood, London WC2

West of England

Sotheby Bearne
Rainbow
Torquay, TQ2 5TG
Telephone: (0803) 26277
Telex: 42661 SBTORG

North West of England and Wales

Sotheby Beresford Adams
Booth Mansions
28 Watergate Street
Chester CH1 1NP
Telephone: (0244) 48833

Edinburgh

*John Robertson**
Sotheby Parke Bernet & Co.
19 Castle Street
Edinburgh EH2 3AH
Telephone: (031) 226 5438
Telegrams: Abinitio, Edinburgh
Telex: 76105

ARGENTINA

*William R. Edbrooke**
Kerteux Antiques
Libertad 846,
Buenos Aires
Telephone: (41) 393 0831
Telegrams: Antiker-Baires

AUSTRALIA

*Bruce Rutherford**
43 Bourke Street
Melbourne, Victoria 3000
Telephone: (03) 63 3900
Telegrams: Abinitio, Melbourne

BELGIUM

*Count Henry de Limburg Stirum**
Sotheby Parke Bernet Belgium,
32 Rue de l'Abbaye,
Brussels 1050
Telephone: (2) 343 5007
Telex: 61339, SPBBXL B

BRAZIL

Rio de Janeiro

*Walter Geyerhahn**
*Cecil Hime**
Rua do Rosario
135-37-2° andar
Rio de Janeiro
Telephone: 252 7495 & 252 9552
Telegrams: Eikos, Rio de Janeiro

Sao Paulo

*Cornelius O.K. Reichenheim**
Alameda Ministro Rocha
Azevedo 391,
Sao Paulo
Telephone: 282-0581

FRANCE

Rear Admiral
*J.A. Templeton-Cotill, C.B.**
Sotheby Parke Bernet
(France) s.a.r.l.
3 Rue de Miromesnil
75008 Paris
Telephone: (1) 266 4060
Telex: 640084 ABINITIO PARIS
Telegrams: Abinitio, France

GERMANY

Munich

*Dr. Ernst Behrens**
Sotheby Parke Bernet
GmbH Munchen,
Odeonsplatz 16, D-8000 Munich 22
Telephone: (89) 22 23 75/6
Telex: 523443 ABNIT DM

Hamburg

*Tatiana von Hessen**
Heilwigstrasse 31A
2000 Hamburg 20
Telephone: (40) 48 69 69
(for correspondence only)

Frankfurt

Sotheby Parke Bernet
GmbH Munchen,
Steinlestrasse 7
D-6000 Frankfurt/M
Telephone: (611) 62 20 27

HOLLAND

Jan Pieter Glerum
Sotheby Mak van Waay B.V.
102 Rokin,
1012 KZ Amsterdam
Telephone: (20) 24 6215/6
Telex: 13267 MAKSO NL
Telegrams: Abinitio, Amsterdam

HONG KONG

Sotheby Parke Bernet
(Hong Kong) Ltd.,
P.O. Box 83,
705 Lane Crawford House,
64-70 Queen's Road Central
Hong Kong
Telephone: (5) 22 5454
Telex: 75486 LANE HX
Telegrams: Abinitio, Hong Kong

IRELAND

*Nicholas Nicholson**
35 Molesworth Street,
Dublin 2
Telephone: (0001) 789368
Consultants: Mrs. Gertrude Hunt &
Mrs. Mary Boydell
Telephone: (0001) 323110 or (0001)
322021

ITALY

Florence

Count Alvise di Robilant
Carmen Gronau (Consultant)
Sotheby Parke Bernet
Italia s.r.l.,
Palazzo Capponi
Via Gino Capponi 26,
50121 Florence
Telephone: (55) 571410
Telex: 572478 ABINIT 1
Telegrams: Abinitio, Firenze

Milan

*Yolanda Galli Zugaro**
Sotheby Parke Bernet
Italia s.r.l.,
Via Montenapoleone 3,
20121 Milan
Telephone: (2) 783907
Telegrams: Abinitio, Milan

Rome

*Jonathan Mennell**
Via del Babuino 41,
00187 Rome
Telephone: (6) 679 0824

MONACO

Dr. S. N. Cristea
Sotheby Parke Bernet
Monaco S.A.,
P.O. Box 45
Sporting D'Hiver,
Place du Casino,
Monte Carlo
Telephone: (93) 30 88 80
Telex: 479471 SPBMON MC

SCANDINAVIA

*Rolf Larson**
Sotheby Parke Bernet
Arsenalsgatan 4,
111 47 Stockholm
Sweden
Telephone: (8) 101478/9
Telex: 17380 SPBCAN S

SOUTH AFRICA

Reinhold H. Cassirer
Sotheby Parke Bernet
South Africa (Proprietary) Ltd.,
4th Floor, Total House,
Smit Street, Cnr. Rissik Street,
Braamfontein, Johannesburg
Telephone: (11) 39-3726/7
Telex: (8) - 3636 SA
Telegrams: Abinitio, Johannesburg

SPAIN

*Edmund Peel**
Sotheby Parke Bernet
Sucursal de Espane
Calle del Prado 18,
1° izda
Madrid 14
Telephone: (34) 232-6488/6572

SWITZERLAND

Zurich

Dr. J. G. Willie in partnership with
Alfred Schwarzenbach
Sotheby Parke Bernet A.G.,
20 Bleicherweg, CH-8022 Zurich
Telephone: (1) 202 0011
Telex: 52380 ABINI CH
Telegrams: Abinitio, Zurich

Geneva

*Nicholas Rayner**
Sotheby Parke Bernet A.G.,
24 Rue de la Cite,
CH-1204 Geneva
Telephone: (22) 21 3377
Telex: 289098 SPB CH
Telegrams: Abinitio, Geneva

SALE 4390

SOTHEBY PARKE BERNET INC.

980 Madison Avenue, New York, N.Y. 10021

Telephone (212) 472-3435, 3436, 3450

Date _____

I desire to place the following bids for sale #4390 to be held on June 6, 1980. These bids are to be executed by Sotheby Parke Bernet up to but not exceeding the amount or amounts specified below. Each bid is *PER LOT,* as indicated, and all bids will be executed and are accepted subject to the *"Conditions of Sale"* and *"Terms of Guarantee"* printed in the catalogue of this sale. **Please see *"Advice to Order Bidders"* on reverse of this bid slip and note that a premium of 10% will be added to the hammer price as part of the total purchase price.**

Name _____
(please print or type)

Address _____
(Street)   (Apt.)

_____
(City)   (State)   (Zip)

Telephone _____

Signed _____

Bank reference or deposit _____
(If bidder is not known to Sotheby Parke Bernet Inc.)

Lot Number	Item	Top limit of Bid *not* including 10% premium (Bid is per lot number as listed in the catalogue) $

If Dealer, please give resale number _____ State _____

IMPORTANT: To facilitate handling, kindly mark envelope: *"Attention —Bid Department."*

BS 1/79

ADVICE TO ORDER BIDDERS

If instructed, Sotheby Parke Bernet Inc. will execute bids and advise prospective purchasers. This service is free. Lots will always be bought as cheaply as is allowed by such other bids and reserves as are on our books or bids executed in competition from the audience. *PLEASE NOTE:* Sotheby Parke Bernet Inc. offers this service as a convenience to its clients who are unable to attend the sale and will not be held responsible for error or failure to execute bids.

Commission bids, when placed by telephone, are accepted only at the sender's risk, and must be confirmed by letter or telegram (Cable address: PARKGAL, NEW YORK)

Please use the bidding slips provided and be sure to carefully note lot numbers and descriptions.

Always quote the sale number of the catalogue to avoid any possible confusion.

Please bid as early as possible. In the event of identical bids, the earliest will take precedence.

"Buy" bids are not accepted. The limit you leave should be the amount to which you would bid if you were to attend the sale.

Each bidding slip should contain bids for one sale only.

Alternative bids can be placed by using the word "OR" between lot numbers.

In order to avoid delay in clearing purchases, buyers unknown to us are advised to make arrangements *before the sale* for payment or for references to be supplied. If such arrangements are not made, checks will be cleared before purchases are delivered. *IMPORTANT NOTE:* Successful bidders will be notified and invoiced within a few days of the sale.

Unsuccessful bidders will not be specifically notified, but will receive a price list indicating results of the sale if a stamped, self-addressed envelope is enclosed with the submitted bid.

Your bid is for the hammer price; a premium of 10% will be added to the hammer price of each lot sold and is payable by you in addition thereto.

AB 1/79

Photographs by
SOTHEBY PARKE BERNET PHOTOGRAPHY DEPT.
Tel. 212/472-3527
Consultant Art Director
ALAN HARTWELL, N.Y.C.
Separations by
TOPPAN PRINTING CO.
Printed in the U.S.A. by
INTELLIGENCER PRINTING CO.

(121518)